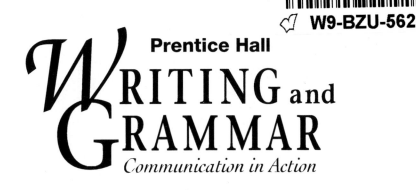

Prentice Hall

WRITING and GRAMMAR

Communication in Action

Prentice Hall

LITERATURE

Timeless Voices, Timeless Themes

Vocabulary and Spelling Practice Book

TEACHER'S EDITION

GOLD LEVEL

OBSOLETE

Prentice Hall

Upper Saddle River, New Jersey
Glenview, Illinois
Needham, Massachusetts

ISBN 0-13-063346-1

4 5 6 7 8 9 10   05

Contents

Vocabulary Practice 1: Prefixes

Prefixes: *extra-, inter-, intra-, intro-, ultra-*

A **prefix** is a word part that is added to the beginning of a base word. A prefix changes the meaning of a word.

The prefix *inter-* means "between." Adding *inter-* to the base word *action*, meaning "activity," makes *interaction*, which means "activity between people or things." Other prefixes have meanings similar to *inter-*.

extra- means "beyond" or "outside of"

inter- means "between," "among," or "in the midst of"

intra- means "in," "into," or "within"

intro- means "inside" or "inward"

ultra- means "beyond" or "exceeding"

A. Think about the meaning of each prefix and base word. Then, write a definition for the word in bold type. Check your definitions in a dictionary.

1. *extra-* + *terrestrial* (relating to the earth) = **extraterrestrial**

   Definition_____

2. *inter-* + *planetary* (relating to the planets) = **interplanetary**

   Definition_____

3. *intra-* + *ocular* (relating to the eye) = **intraocular**

   Definition_____

4. *ultra-* + *sound* (tone of human hearing) = **ultrasound**

   Definition_____

5. *intro-* + *spection* (the act of examining) = **introspection**

   Definition_____

6. *extra-* + *curricular* (relating to courses of study) = **extracurricular**

   Definition_____

7. *inter-* + *dependent* (relying on another) = **interdependent**

   Definition_____

8. *intra-* + *venous* (relating to veins) = **intravenous**

   Definition_____

9. *ultra-* + *modernist* (one who believes in current views) = **ultramodernist**

   Definition_____

10. *intro-* + *version* (the act of turning) = **introversion**

    Definition_____

B. On separate paper, make a list of three words using each prefix. Then, write a sentence using each word.

Vocabulary Practice 2: Prefixes

Prefixes: *ante-, fore-, pre-, pro-, post-*

A **prefix** is a word part that is added to the beginning of a base word. A prefix changes the meaning of the word.

The prefix *fore-* means "before." Adding *fore-* to the base word *sight* meaning "vision," makes *foresight*, which means "seeing or knowing before something happens." The prefixes *ante-, pre-,* and *pro-* also mean "before." The prefix *post-* means "after."

A. Add the prefixes to the base words. Write the definitions of the prefixed words. Check your definitions in a dictionary. The first one is an example.

1. The prefix *fore-* means "before in time."

   a. _____fore_____ **tell**: to tell before something happens; to predict

   b. _____ **cast**: _____

   c. _____ **shadow**: _____

2. The prefix *ante-* means "before," "forward," or "in front of."

   a. _____ **date**: _____

   b. _____ **chamber**: _____

   c. _____ **mortem**: _____

3. The prefix *pre-* means "earlier than" or "prior."

   a. _____ **arrange**: _____

   b. _____ **mature**: _____

   c. _____ **judge**: _____

4. The prefix *pro-* means "forward" or "in favor of."

   a. _____ **claim**: _____

   b. _____ **active**: _____

   c. _____ **long**: _____

5. The prefix *post-* means "after."

   a. _____ **millenial**: _____

   b. _____ **graduate**: _____

   c. _____ **operative**: _____

B. Write the words you formed in Exercise A in these sentences.

1. Sam took a _____ role in helping his candidate win the election.

2. The attorneys and clients met in a courthouse _____ to discuss a settlement.

3. Celebrations were recorded for _____ children—those born after A.D. 2000.

4. It was _____ to announce technological success without testing.

5. In retrospect, the circumstances did _____ the story's climax.

Vocabulary Practice 3: Prefixes

Prefixes: *a-*, *in-*, *non-*, *un-*

The **prefix** is a word part that is added to the beginning of a base word. A prefix changes the meaning of the word.

The prefix *in-* means "not." Adding *in-* to the base word *adequate*, meaning "sufficient," makes *inadequate*, which means "not sufficient." The prefixes *a-*, *in-*, *non-*, and *un-* also mean "not," or "without."

A. Add the base word to each prefix to make the new word that matches the definition.

satisfactory	appropriate	hospitable	typical	allergic
restricted	symmetrical	warranted	harmonious	informed

1. non _____ means "*not* caused by extreme reaction or sensitivity"

2. un _____ means "*not* meeting a standard or requirement"

3. in _____ means "*not* suitable"

4. a _____ means "*not* the usual or of a certain type"

5. in _____ means "*not* in accord or agreement"

6. un _____ means "*not* having basis or justification"

7. non _____ means "*not* binding or confining; not limited"

8. un _____ means "*not* knowing, educated, or knowledgable"

9. a _____ means "*not* capable of division into equal halves"

10. in _____ means "*not* friendly or receptive to guests"

B. Write five other words used with each prefix. Check your words in a dictionary.

	non-	*un-*	*in-*	*a-*
1.	_____	_____	_____	_____
2.	_____	_____	_____	_____
3.	_____	_____	_____	_____
4.	_____	_____	_____	_____
5.	_____	_____	_____	_____

C. Unscramble these four words, which have prefixes. Write the definitions.

1. enlerubila _____

2. csifonecpin _____

3. romala _____

4. idecential _____

Vocabulary Practice 4: Prefixes

Prefixes: *mon-, mono-, uni-*

A **prefix** is a word part that is added to the beginning of a base word. A prefix changes the meaning of a word.

The prefix *uni-* means "one." Adding *uni-* to the base word *cycle*, meaning "wheel or circle," makes *unicycle*, which means" a one-wheeled vehicle." The prefixes *mon-* and *mono-* also mean "one."

A. Underline the words in these sentences with the prefixes meaning "one."

1. Stereophonic sound systems replaced monaural record players, which became collectibles.

2. An imaginary animal depicted as a horse is called a unicorn.

3. Chad's nervousness caused him to read his report in a monotone.

4. In many airports, a monorail takes passengers from parking lots to terminals.

5. One form of marriage custom practiced in many societies is monogamy.

6. The universal theme of the conference attracted people from all over the world.

7. Monaco is a monarchy ruled by the Grimaldi family since the thirteenth century.

8. Some hospitals require the nursing staff to conform to a uniform dress code.

9. Children who are monolingual study other languages in school.

10. The unilateral report, read by its author, presented a very narrow view.

B. For each word you underlined, write the prefix and base word beside the definition.

Prefix	Base Word	Definition of the Underlined Word
1. _____	_____	means "using one tone or sound with no variety"
2. _____	_____	means "a train that runs on one track"
3. _____	_____	means "the custom of marrying only one person"
4. _____	_____	means "government ruled by a single person"
5. _____	_____	means "including the entire or whole world as one"
6. _____	_____	means "knowing or using one language"
7. _____	_____	means "a mythological one-horned animal"
8. _____	_____	means "having one or the same manner or degree"
9. _____	_____	means "a single speaker path for sound"
10. _____	_____	means "concerned with one person or side of a subject"

C. Write two more words with each prefix and write the definitions.

_____

_____

_____

Vocabulary Practice 5: Suffixes

Suffixes: *-ant, -ar, -er, -ist, -or*

A **suffix** is a word part that is added to the end of a base word. A suffix changes the meaning of a word.

The suffix *-or* means "one who." Adding *-or* to the base word *act*, meaning "perform," makes *actor*, which means "one who acts." The suffixes *-ant, -ar, -er, and -ist* also mean "one who does, makes, or is concerned with."

A. Write the base word and suffix for each word. Some words require a spelling change. Then, write the number of the description that belongs with each word. The first one is an example.

	Base Word and Suffix	Description Matches	Description
1. activist	active and -ist	5	1. writes a column or article for a newspaper or magazine
2. defendant	_____	_____	2. settles differences between people
3. conductor	_____	_____	3. helps or aides another in a task or job
4. specialist	_____	_____	4. is skilled in giving powerful speeches
5. designer	_____	_____	5. takes an active role in issues or causes
6. orator	_____	_____	6. has a very specific occupation or area of learning
7. machinist	_____	_____	7. makes laws for a political area
8. employer	_____	_____	8. has been charged with an offense in a court case
9. accountant	_____	_____	9. is competing for an award
10. columnist	_____	_____	10. hires and pays wages to employees
11. legislator	_____	_____	11. has advanced study in a particular field
12. finalist	_____	_____	12. figures tax returns or business expenses
13. arbitrator	_____	_____	13. leads an orchestra or band
14. assistant	_____	_____	14. works with machinery
15. scholar	_____	_____	15. creates plans for a design or style

B. On separate paper, write five words with each suffix that means "one who."

Vocabulary Practice 6: Suffixes

Suffixes: -ic, -ile, -ive

A **suffix** is a word part that is added to the end of a base word. A suffix changes the meaning of a word.

The suffix -ic means "like." Adding -ic to the word mime, meaning "to imitate," makes mimic, which means "to imitate, copy, or ridicule." Other suffixes with similar meanings are -ile, which means "having to do with" or "like," and -ive, which means "relating to."

A. Write the suffix that is added to the base word to make a new word. Write the new word that matches the definition. Some words change spelling when adding the suffix. Check your spelling in a dictionary.

Base Word	Suffix	New Word	Definition
1. electron	-ic	electronic	means "related to principles of electricity"
2. optimist	_____	_____	means "expecting the best outcome"
3. fantasy	_____	_____	means "unbelievable; not real"
4. project	_____	_____	means "designed to be thrown or hurled forward"
5. support	_____	_____	means "promoting interests or causes"
6. frag- (frail)	_____	_____	means "delicate; easily broken"
7. select	_____	_____	means "choosing carefully"
8. success	_____	_____	means "following in order"
9. magnet	_____	_____	means "attracting iron, steel, and other materials"
10. tact	_____	_____	means "a plan or means to accomplish a goal"

B. Write the words you formed in Exercise A in the following passage. Use the context to help you determine the correct word.

Nigel became interested in science when he put magnets on a tiny car and built a

_____ road. He liked to work in his basement making

_____ gadgets like toys with wires and batteries. His grandfather

worked with Nigel and was very _____ of Nigel's interests in sci-

ence. Nigel was very _____ in choosing his projects. Once, how-

ever, he and Grandfather built a rocket and launch pad that turned into a disaster. As

Nigel was assembling the rocket for a practice launch, a small piece of metal became a

_____, without warning, and flew through the air at great speed. It

destroyed parts of the construction that were _____, or easily broken.

Fortunately, Nigel and his grandfather were _____ about rebuilding

this project. They discussed a _____ for creating a successful rocket project.

C. On a separate piece of paper, write an ending to the story, using the two words that you did not use in the passage.

Vocabulary Practice 7: Suffixes

Suffixes: *-hood, -ity, -ness*

A **suffix** is a word part that is added to the end of a base word. A suffix changes the meaning of a word.

The suffix *-ness* means "a state or a quality of being." Adding *-ness* to the base word *kind*, meaning "gentle," makes *kindness*, which means "being gentle." Other suffixes with similar meanings are: *-hood*, which means "a group" or "class of;" *-ness*, which means "condition" or "quality of;" and *-ity*, which means "degree of being" or "character."

A. Add the suffix to the words in each column.

-hood	**–ness**	**-ity**
1. brother _____	1. awkward _____	1. individual _____
2. neighbor _____	2. like _____	2. active _____
3. parent _____	3. responsive _____	3. curious _____
4. child _____	4. friendly _____	4. rapid _____
5. state _____	5. astute _____	5. original _____

B. Read each pair of sentences. Write the words you formed above in the second sentence of each pair. The clue is in the first sentence.

1. A parent has many responsibilities as a child's guardian.

   The responsibilities of _____ include attention to a child's safety.

2. Carol is an individual who gets involved in lots of creative activities.

   She demonstrates her _____ in art class with a unique style of painting.

3. Joanne, who is fifteen, looks exactly like her young mother.

   In fact, the _____ is so astonishing that they appear to be twins.

4. Curious, four-year-old Jake wandered around the pet shop.

   His _____ got the better of him, and he pulled a fishbowl off the shelf.

5. The new doctor already had a reputation for being responsive to patients.

   When Susan had an emergency, the doctor's _____ saved her life.

6. Do you know when Alaska joined the United States?

   Alaska was admitted for _____ in 1959.

7. People will soon be commuting on the new rapid train from Boston to New York.

   The _____ of trains compares favorably with that of air travel.

8. Jasper was a friendly dog, happily greeting everyone who entered the yard.

   One day his _____ turned into aggressiveness when some children teased him.

9. As a child, Ineka traveled with her parents all over the world.

   As an adult, she had wonderful memories of her _____ experiences.

10. The immigrant was astute about the customs of her new country.

    Her _____ helped her handle difficult situations in her new life.

Vocabulary Practice 8: Suffixes

Suffixes: *-cy, -ion, -ment, -sion, -tion*

A **suffix** is a word part that is added to the end of a base word. A suffix changes the meaning of a word.

The suffix *-ment* means "act or quality of." Adding *-ment* to the base word *agree*, meaning "consent," makes *agreement*, which means "the act of consenting." Other suffixes with similar meanings are: *-ion, -sion, -tion*, which means "act or condition of"; and *-cy*, which means "state or position of."

A. Underline the words having the suffixes listed above.

1. The principal announced scholarship awards at the commencement.

2. Flowers were an expression of the family's sympathy and friendship.

3. The neighbors settled their disagreement by creating a workable solution.

4. At the conclusion of the trial, the jury delivered the verdict.

5. Students studied at the library to improve their concentration on homework.

6. Every adult made a commitment to work in the relief effort.

7. The juxtaposition of the two entrances presented a problem for walking traffic.

8. The Secretary of State attempted to resolve the crisis with diplomacy.

9. Part of the plan for student enrichment was a monthly trip to the art museum.

10. Life returned to normalcy many weeks after the tornado.

B. Match the words you underlined in Exercise A with their definitions.

_____ 1. means "that which makes richer or improves by adding a desired quality"

_____ 2. means "having the normal or usual pattern"

_____ 3. means "fixed attention on a subject or goal"

_____ 4. means "side by side or close together"

_____ 5. means "a difference of opinion"

_____ 6. means "the act of outwardly communicating thoughts or ideas"

_____ 7. means "the ceremony for the conferring of degrees or diplomas"

_____ 8. means "an obligation or pledge"

_____ 9. means "the end or termination"

_____ 10. means "the conducting of political relations and government negotiations"

C. Write the base words of the underlined words in Exercise A. Use a dictionary, if necessary.

-ion, -sion, or -tion	*-ment*	*-cy*
_____	_____	_____
_____	_____	_____
_____	_____	
_____	_____	

Vocabulary Practice 9: Word Roots

Word roots: -spec-, -spect-, -scop-, -vis-, -vid-

A **word root** forms the basic part of a word and gives the word its primary meaning. Prefixes and suffixes add specific meaning to word roots. If you know the meaning of a root, you can often figure out the meaning of a whole word.

The word root -vis- means "look" or "see." Adding the suffix -ible, meaning "able" or "capable," to the root -vis- makes *visible*, which means "being seen." Other word roots with similar meanings are: -vid-, which means "to see" or "to look at;" -scope-, which means "to watch" or "to spy;" -spec- and -spect-, which mean "to see" or "to observe."

A. Underline the roots in these words.

specimen	**improvise**	**supervision**	**visionary**	**kaleidoscope**
spectrum	**seismoscope**	**evidence**	**circumspect**	**periscope**

B. Using the root meanings and sentence clues, write definitions for the words in italics. Check your definitions in a dictionary.

1. The scientist used a *periscope* to observe life at the bottom of the ocean.

   Definition_____

2. The quilts sewn for charity displayed the full *spectrum* of colors.

   Definition_____

3. After the top-secret meeting, those in attendance were *circumspect* in discussions.

   Definition_____

4. As children, we always enjoyed the beautiful patterns in a *kaleidoscope*.

   Definition_____

5. The President's job as *visionary* is to plan for the country's future.

   Definition_____

6. Ships and planes use instruments called *gyroscopes* and gyrocompasses to keep them level.

   Definition_____

7. The lab took a small soil *specimen* to conduct a test on its nitrogen content.

   Definition_____

8. Anthropologists gathered bones, teeth, and the skull of a dinosaur they found in the forest and reported their findings as *evidence* of another genus of dinosaurs.

   Definition_____

9. The actor forgot his lines, but he was able to *improvise*, to the delight of the audience.

   Definition_____

10. A *seismoscope* is an essential instrument for recording earthquake data.

    Definition_____

Vocabulary Practice 10: Word Roots

Word roots: *-pass-*, *-path-*, *-sens-*, *-sent-*, *-tang-*, *-tact-*

A **word root** forms the basic part of a word and gives the word its primary meaning. Prefixes and suffixes add specific meaning to word roots. If you know the meaning of a root, you can often figure out the meaning of a whole word.

The root *-sent-* means "feel" or "think." Adding the suffix *-dis*, meaning "not" or "away from," to the root *-sent-* makes *dissent*, which means "feeling against something." Other word roots with similar meanings are: *-sens-*, which means "feel" or "think;" *-pass-* and *-path-*, which mean "feel" or "suffer;" and *-tact-* and *-tang-*, which mean "touch."

A. Write the word that belongs in the sentence. Underline the root in each answer choice.

1. Jake explained to his little brother why it was _____ to wear a helmet when riding his bike.

   tangible   **tactile**   **sensible**

2. The busy nurse was still very _____ to her patients' needs.

   sensitive   **passive**   **tactful**

3. Feelings and thoughts are _____, but they are a major aspect of our self-expression.

   sympathy   **telepathy**   **intangible**

4. Watching the news, Helen felt great _____ for the homeless.

   tactics   **compassion**   **sensations**

5. When Anne received her final exam scores, she felt she had a _____ reward for her extra effort all semester.

   tangible   **sensual**   **passionate**

6. The earthquake demolished most of the buildings in the city, but the newspaper building was still _____.

   tactless   **pathetic**   **intact**

7. Holly looked for a card with the perfect _____ for Jessica.

   sensation   **sentiment**   **contact**

8. The politician gave a fiery, or _____, speech about animals' rights.

   pathetic   **impassioned**   **tangled**

9. A meteorological report gave _____ information about tornadoes in the region, but it gave in-depth information about hurricanes.

   tangential   **passionate**   **sentimental**

10. The reporter used a very clever _____ to interview the senator.

    sensor   **tactic**   **pathology**

B. On other paper, explain answer choices 1, 3, and 4 in Exercise A, referring to the meaning of the root in your answer.

Vocabulary Practice 11: Word Roots

Word roots: -solu-, -solv-

A **word root** forms the basic part of a word and gives the word its primary meaning. Prefixes and suffixes add specific meaning to word roots. If you know the meaning of a root, you can often figure out the meaning of a whole word.

The Latin words *solutus* and *solvere* mean "to loosen" or "to dissolve." Roots formed from these Latin words are spelled -solu- or -solv-, and mean "to loosen" or "to dissolve." Adding the suffix -tion, meaning "the condition of," to the word root -solu- makes *solution*, which means "that which is dissolved" or "a liquid."

A. Underline all the words with the roots -solu- and -solv- in this passage.

Dr. Distraction walked with resolve into his chemistry lab believing that the mystery was solvable. The day before, he had used a solute that had turned azure blue as it dissolved. Then, overnight, the solution had turned clear! He couldn't remember which solvents he had used, so he tried mixing many combinations of soluble chemicals. Finally, as he mixed the last combination of liquid and powder, the mystery was solved. Now Dr. Distraction could absolve himself of making a mistake with his own formula! What is your solution to the mystery?

B. Using the definitions of the prefixes and suffixes below and sentence clues in the passage, write the words you underlined beside their definitions. One word has two meanings.

Prefixes	Suffixes
ab- (away)	*-ble* (able)
dis- (apart)	*-able* (able)
re- (again)	*-ent* (condition)
	-tion (condition)

1. _____ means "liquid mixtures that can break down other substances"

2. _____ means "a fixed purpose; firm determination"

3. _____ means "found a solution to a problem"

4. _____ means "can be dissolved"

5. _____ means "melted; became liquid"

6. _____ means "to set free from guilt or blame"

7. _____ means "an answer to a problem"

8. _____ means "capable of being explained"

9. _____ means "mixture of solids, liquids, or gases"

10. _____ means "a substance that has dissolved or changed in a process"

C. On another piece of paper, write a *solution* to the mystery using words with the roots -solv- and -solu-.

Vocabulary Practice 12: Word Roots

Word roots: -prim-, -prime-, -primo-, -prot-, -proto-

A **word root** forms the basic part of a word and gives the word its primary meaning. Prefixes and suffixes add specific meaning to word roots. If you know the meaning of a root, you can often figure out the meaning of a whole word.

The Latin word *primus* means "first." Many words and phrases in English have the Latin roots -prim-, -prime-, -primo-, -prot-, and -proto-, all meaning "first." Adding the suffix -ary, meaning "relating to," to the word root -prim- makes *primary*, which means "first in time or order."

A. Underline the words in these sentences with a root that means "first." Then, write a definition for each underlined word. Check your definitions in a dictionary.

1. Congressional members read the protocol, and then debated this original draft of a bill.

   Definition_____

2. The human brain today is much larger than that of primitive humans.

   Definition_____

3. Da Vinci's famous flying machine design was a prototype for the first airplane.

   Definition_____

4. In a drama, the protagonist sometimes shares center stage with the villain.

   Definition_____

5. A good diet includes adequate amounts of protein as well as other nutrients.

   Definition_____

6. Greenwich, England, is the location of the prime meridian, or 0° longitude, from which all other lines of longitude are counted east and west.

   Definition_____

7. The manager discussed the company's primary account, or principal financial source.

   Definition_____

8. On the opening night of the ballet, the understudy took the principal role for the evening.

   Definition_____

9. Adam, who became a primatologist, studied the earliest mammals.

   Definition_____

10. Benjamin, the eldest son, claimed his family's inheritance, or primogeniture.

    Definition_____

B. On other paper, write five more words with prefixes that mean "first."

Vocabulary Practice 13: Word Roots

Word roots: -sta-, -stat-

A **word root** forms the basic part of a word and gives the word its primary meaning. Prefixes and suffixes add specific meaning to word roots. If you know the meaning of a root, you can often figure out the meaning of a whole word.

The Latin root *-stare-* means "to stand." Words formed with this root are spelled *-sta-* or *-stat-*. Adding the prefix *un-*, meaning "not," and the suffix "*-le*," meaning "able," to the root *-stab-* makes *unstable*, which means "not able to stand."

A. Underline the word in each sentence with the root *-sta-* or *-stat-*. Then, circle the word that defines the word you underlined.

1. When Henry's status in the company changed, he decided to find another job.

   salary   **office**   **position**

2. Huge layoffs caused economic instability and eventually resulted in bankruptcy.

   unevenness   **uprising**   **steadfastness**

3. Shelby rode her stationary bike every evening to work off tension.

   motorized   **manual**   **standing**

4. Students were ecstatic over the announcement of a delay in the school's opening.

   despairing   **overjoyed**   **disbelieving**

5. The speaker's stature in politics drew a capacity crowd to the auditorium.

   notoriety   **knowledge**   **importance**

6. The city's mayor established a memorial fund for the accident victims.

   declared   **contributed**   **awarded**

7. The doctor ordered fluids and medications to stabilize the child's vital signs.

   force   **balance**   **affect**

8. Corporations use national employment and income statistics to plan their futures.

   data   **evaluation**   **codes**

9. Weather patterns were stagnant in July, resulting in weeks of high humidity.

   active   **unsettled**   **motionless**

10. The baseball player's stance was comical, and he amused the fans in every game.

    uniform   **pose**   **attitude**

B. On another piece of paper, write a response to each question. Use the boldface word in your answer, and underline the word. Use a dictionary, if necessary.

standard   1. What kinds of rules for arriving and leaving school are enforced?

statute(s)   2. What law governs the age for getting a driver's license in your state?

rheostat   3. Who might use an instrument for regulating electrical current?

stable   4. How can you give a puppy a good home and environment?

stagnate   5. Why might a pond become unfit for fish and other life?

Vocabulary Practice 14: Synonyms

A **synonym** is a word similar in meaning to another word. Knowing synonyms will improve your speaking and writing vocabulary.

Example: *Loyal* is a synonym for *faithful*.

A. Write the synonym for each numbered word.

naive	**suffice**	**endurance**	**waver**	**pursue**
legacy	**articulate**	**perpetuate**	**focused**	**astute**

1. inheritance _____
2. stamina _____
3. explain _____
4. continue _____
5. keen _____

6. sway back and forth _____
7. intent _____
8. be enough _____
9. follow _____
10. unsophisticated _____

B. Write the boldface words from Exercise A in this passage.

Jason was _____, or shy, about making his own way in the

world. He tended to _____ in making a decision about his future.

He was _____ on letting the future make itself known to him.

Jason could _____ his reasons for not deciding what he wanted to

do as graduation approached. Perhaps he would _____ the family

name, now on the restaurant his great-grandfather had built. Running a restaurant re-

quired commitment and _____, both of which Jason had in no

short supply. It was his _____ from his grandfather and father.

Also, he thought he might _____ his interest in technology. He was

very _____ about technological developments and had his own

ideas for inventions. For now, just thinking about all the options for his future would

_____.

C. Using a dictionary or thesaurus, write three synonyms for each word.

1. commitment _____
2. inherited _____
3. options _____

D. The word *articulate*, used as a verb in the passage, is also an adjective. Write a definition for *articulate* as used in this sentence:

Nancy is an *articulate* speaker and is often asked to address the assembly.

_____

_____

Vocabulary Practice 15: Synonyms

A **synonym** is a word similar in meaning to another word. Knowing synonyms will improve your speaking and writing vocabulary.

Example: *Truthful* is a synonym for *honest.*

A. Write the boldface word that belongs with each set of synonyms.

raze	opaque	foible	reconciliation	opulent
blithe	circuitous	rudimentary	coagulate	befuddle

1. confuse, bewilder, _____

2. happy, carefree, _____

3. indirect, roundabout, _____

4. congeal, clot, _____

5. imperfection, fault, _____

6. nontransparent, cloudy, _____

7. destroy, ruin, _____

8. lavish, luxurious, _____

9. settlement, agreement, _____

10. basic, elementary, _____

B. Write the boldface word from Exercise A that completes each sentence.

1. Arithmetic skills are the _____ form of all higher mathematics.

2. As we watched, bulldozers began to _____ the oldest houses in the block.

3. The decorator used _____ window shades to block the outside light.

4. The partners agreed to an immediate _____ to settle the dispute.

5. Taking the _____ route to the ball game caused us to miss the first inning.

6. Buying her first car, Soo Yung could not afford the _____ leather interior.

7. Tyler waited for the blood to _____, so the doctor would let him leave.

8. Amy was a _____ spirit, always cheerful, optimistic, and positive.

9. The one _____ that was Hank's downfall was his habit of procrastinating.

10. The store changed the location of items, which _____(d) customers.

C. On other paper, write as many synonyms as you can for *circuitous, blithe, rudimentary, opaque,* and *foible.*

Name _____ Date _____

Vocabulary Practice 16: Synonyms

A **synonym** is a word similar in meaning to another word. In a synonym analogy, both pairs of words are synonyms.

> **Example:** In the following analogy, the first pair of words is a synonym. Which pair of words completes the analogy?
>
> FORECAST:PREDICT:: _____
>
> a. advise:recommend   b. request:respond   c. inform:question

The answer is ADVISE:RECOMMEND, which are synonyms.

A. Complete each analogy by choosing the letter of the pair of words that show a synonym relationship. Use a dictionary or thesaurus, if necessary.

1. REJECT:DECLINE:: _____
   a. deny:define   b. dismiss:accept   c. confound:confuse

2. GROTESQUE:REPULSIVE:: _____
   a. conglomeration:mixture   b. unfamiliar:awkward   c. attractive:unusual

3. FRET:WORRY:: _____
   a. deliver:purchase   b. delineate:describe   c. scold:reassure

4. MOCK:RIDICULE:: _____
   a. choose:contribute   b. choose:deny   c. emulate:copy

5. ADMIRE:PRAISE:: _____
   a. guile:innocence   b. stage:drama   c. novice:newcomer

6. HUMOROUS:AMUSING:: _____
   a. poor:substantial   b. insolvent:bankrupt   c. secure:unsteady

7. SENTIMENTAL:NOSTALGIC:: _____
   a. sensitive:sensible   b. complimentary:final   c. laudable:admirable

8. ANONYMOUS:UNKNOWN:: _____
   a. meticulous:detailed   b. metric:digital   c. cautious:unguarded

9. DISPUTE:CHALLENGE:: _____
   a. pacify:forgive   b. needle:annoy   c. argue:concede

10. PROSPERITY:FORTUNE:: _____
    a. ancient:antiquity   b. squander:save   c. thrifty:poverty

B. Write a synonym to complete each analogy.

1. UNKEMPT:SLOPPY::PUNCTUAL: _____

2. PLEASING:AESTHETIC::DISTASTEFUL: _____

3. CHILDISH:IMMATURE::SOPHISTICATED: _____

4. PAY:COMPENSATE::RECOGNIZE: _____

5. JUSTIFY:DEFEND::COMPLAIN: _____

Vocabulary Practice 17: Antonyms

An **antonym** is a word that is opposite in meaning to another word. Knowing antonyms will improve your speaking and writing vocabulary.

Example: *Optimist* is an antonym for *pessimist.*

A. Write the boldface word that is an antonym for the two synonyms given. Use a dictionary or thesaurus to check your answers.

alien	**defiant**	**genteel**	**introspective**	**judicious**
literal	**mute**	**reject**	**subtle**	**sullen**

Synonyms **Antonyms**

1. direct, frank _____

2. cooperative, willing _____

3. accept, select _____

4. cheerful, happy _____

5. unwise, indiscreet _____

6. unprecise, inaccurate _____

7. vocal, spoken _____

8. unrefined, unpolished _____

9. unreflective, thoughtless _____

10. familiar, known _____

B. Write the boldface word from Exercise A that belongs in the first part of each sentence. Then, write a sentence ending using an antonym for the word you wrote in the sentence.

Example: Elderly Mrs. Johnson was known as a genteel person because she was very refined, extremely polite, and well-mannered with everyone.

1. The contestant was so excited and nervous she became _____

   when _____.

2. To stop the _____ child from screaming, Leslie _____

   _____.

3. As a shy, _____ teenager, Patti greeted people she had never met by

   _____.

4. The usually good-natured toddler became moody and _____ when

   he entered the doctor's office and _____.

5. Every jury member was _____ about keeping silence regarding the

   details of the case after the judge _____.

Vocabulary Practice 18: Antonyms

An **antonym** is a word that is opposite in meaning to another word. Knowing antonyms will improve your speaking and writing vocabulary.

Example: *Enemy* is an antonym for *friend*.

A. Read each pair of sentences. In the second sentence, write the boldface word that is an antonym for the underlined word or words in the first sentence.

chaste	**commence**	**crass**	**discreet**	**dishearten**
neglected	**placid**	**ravenous**	**spurn**	**verbose**

1. The Smiths loved to take care of their lawn and garden.

   The lawn and garden were _____ when the owners were out of town.

2. The teacher reminded students to be polite and courteous with the speaker.

   Unfortunately, one student was _____ and was asked to leave the assembly.

3. Shirley decided she would accept the invitation everyone waited to receive.

   It would not be polite to _____ a gracious invitation to this special event.

4. The ceremonies will conclude promptly at eleven o'clock.

   We will be in our seats at eight o'clock when the speeches _____ .

5. Alice was satisfied with a light breakfast and left early for the ski slopes.

   After skiing all afternoon, she was _____ and arrived early for dinner.

6. Marj sailed close to shore because the ocean was becoming rough.

   The lake was _____ and clear, so we could almost see to the bottom.

7. Nick's neighbor was friendly, but usually not conversational.

   However, he was _____ when he talked about his favorite sports teams.

8. Jenny's classmates were usually public about the plans for her party.

   It was difficult to be _____ about the party when Jenny was around.

9. Coach Williams always encouraged the soccer team and supported them.

   The coach tried not to _____ the players with the news of his leaving the team.

10. The storybook princess had an impure heart and led her prince to destruction.

    The princess's stepsister, on the other hand, was _____ and saved the prince.

B. Write antonyms for these words that are different from those used in the sentences above. Check your answers in a thesaurus or dictionary.

1. **neglected** _____

2. **commence** _____

3. **discreet** _____

4. **verbose** _____

5. **placid** _____

Name _____ Date _____

Vocabulary Practice 19: Antonyms

An **antonym** is a word that is opposite in meaning to another word. In an antonym analogy, both pairs of words are antonyms.

Example: In the following analogy, the first pair of words is an antonym. Complete the analogy by choosing the word pair that is an antonym.
FAVORABLE:UNFAVORABLE:: _____.

  a. real:false   b. likely:possible   c. pretty:attractive

The answer is REAL:FALSE, which are antonyms.

A. To complete each analogy, choose the letter for the pair of words that shows an antonym relationship. Use a dictionary or thesaurus, if necessary.

1. EDUCATED:UNLEARNED: _____
    a. confined:limited   b. ambulatory:immobile   c. risk:chance

2. HARMONY:DISCORD:: _____
    a. logical:wise   b. old-fashioned:antique   c. audible:faint

3. PERFECT:FLAWED:: _____
    a. contrite:sorry   b. unpleasant:cordial   c. anxiety:concern

4. SLIGHT:ROBUST:: _____
    a. humorous:funny   b. demonstrative:unemotional   c. vague:obtuse

5. DENIAL:ADMISSION:: _____
    a. chief:principal   b. grateful:appreciative   c. depreciate:increase

6. PRIVATE: PUBLIC:: _____
    a. introverted:timid   b. incoherent:articulate   c. mistake:error

7. LAUNCH:TERMINATE:: _____
    a. limited:unrestricted   b. sustain:support   c. victory:triumph

8. OBSCURE:RECOGNIZED:: _____
    a. downhearted:happy   b. official:authorized   c. mundane:worldly

9. TOLERANCE:PREJUDICE:: _____
    a.somber:gloomy   b. pallid:colorful   c. clumsily:awkwardly

10. DOWDY:FASHIONABLE:: _____
    a. spendthrift:miserly   b. lavish:reckless   c. pensive:thoughtful

B. Write an antonym to complete each analogy.

1. SIMPLE:COMPLICATED::BANAL: _____

2. SECURE:UNSURE::SVELTE: _____

3. AMBITIOUS:LAZY::CEASE: _____

4. COMPASSIONATE:INDIFFERENT::ARROGANT: _____

5. DISMISS:RETAIN::AVOW: _____

Vocabulary Practice 20: Synonym and Antonym Review

A **synonym** is a word with the same or nearly the same meaning as another word. An **antonym** is a word that is opposite in meaning to another word.

A. Choose the word that has *most nearly the same meaning* as the word in italics.

1. The speaker arrived on time to *commence* the scholarship awards.

   a. repeat   b. initiate   c. summarize   d. conclude

2. Marie was *discreet* in dealing with the competition for her business.

   a. outgoing   b. inappropriate   c. friendly   d. cautious

3. To her mother, Ginny's soft cries were *audible* and not to be disregarded.

   a. perceptible   b. familiar   c. placid   d. auspicious

4. The visitors were *verbose* when meeting the mayor to plan the exchange program.

   a. alien   b. foreign   c. talkative   d. sullen

5. When Mr. Jaynes's financial portfolio began to *depreciate*, he called his accountant.

   a. devalue   b. escalate   c. unravel   d. demonstrate

6. Allen was *contrite* as he approached his best friend ready to make amends.

   a. controlled   b. hopeful   c. sullen   d. apologetic

7. When it was time to leave for college, Ken was *introspective* about his future.

   a. reflective   b. concerned   c. downhearted   d. mundane

8. The new neighbors are *judicious* about their children's playmates.

   a. ravenous   b.incoherent   c. demonstrative   d. discerning

B. Choose the word that is *opposite* in meaning to the word in italics.

1. Cheryl was *articulate* when talking about her computer and her job.

   a. ineloquent   b. direct   c. haughty   d. opaque

2. Professional sports require a high level of *endurance*.

   a. compensation   b. routine   c. fatigue   d. stamina

3. After many years of feuding, family members had a *reconciliation*.

   a. reunion   b. celebration   c. conspiracy   d. disagreement

4. Taking art classes again was *rudimentary*, but necessary after years of not painting.

   a. basic   b. advanced   c. mundane   d. laudable

5. When the bank announced that it was *insolvent*, customers closed their accounts.

   a. merging   b. foreclosed   c. purchased   d. profitable

6. The couple drove along the shoreline, a *circuitous* route, and took three hours to arrive.

   a. magnificent   b. circular   c. direct   d. uneventful

7. Susan was known for her *laudable* achievements throughout her life.

   a. meritorious   b. dishonorable   c. questionable   d. worthy

8. People express *adulation* for someone they admire in the public world.

   a. respect   b. admiration   c. worship   d. contempt

C. Write one synonym and one antonym for these words: *opaque, defiant, dishearten, naive.*

Vocabulary Practice 21: Analogies

An **analogy** is a relationship between pairs of words. In an analogy, the relationship between the first pair of words is the same as the relationship between the second pair of words.

Example: In one type of analogy, the relationship between words is "a part of." In PAGE:BOOK, *page* is "a part of" a *book*. In another type of analogy, the first word is "a type of" the second word in the pair. In NOVEL:BOOK, a novel is "a type of" book.

A. Determine the relationship in the first pair of words. To complete the analogy, circle the letter of the word pair with the same relationship.

1. STEPS:DANCE:: _____
   a. stem:petal
   b. stripe:flag
   c. shade:lamp
   d. garden:tomato
   e. can:bottle

2. WATERSKIING:SPORT:: _____
   a. brick:walk
   b. apple:crust
   c. vet:dog
   d. China:Great Wall
   e. maple:leaf

3. SOLOIST:CHORUS _____
   a. conductor:symphony
   b. kite:wind
   c. officer:badge
   d. bicycle:safety
   e. menu:entree

4. LEADER:TROOP _____
   a. boy:child
   b. sail:launch
   c. flue:chimney
   d. tooth:brush
   e. time:watch

5. BACKHOE:EQUIPMENT _____
   a. science:microscope
   b. gasoline:car
   c. satire:comedy
   d. lecture:auditorium
   e. cartoon:newspaper

6. COLLAR:SHIRT _____
   a. book:read
   b. oven:stove
   c. desk:chair
   d. car:garage
   e. knob:radio

7. SIAMESE:CAT _____
   a. scenery:stage
   b. Vermont:leaves
   c. rain:lake
   d. bank:building
   e. skirt:shirt

8. NAME:LABEL _____
   a. sign:street
   b. weekend:holiday
   c. inches:yards
   d. vacation:plan
   e. beach:umbrella

9. SAHARA:DESERT _____
   a. boundary:line
   b. river:stream
   c. cake:dessert
   d. ape:monkey
   e. canoe:rapids

10. CANVAS:PAINTING _____
    a. artist:museum
    b. moderator:panel
    c. music:musician
    d. books:librarian
    e. cook:chef

B. Complete these "part of" and "type of" analogies.

1. RULER:TOOL::HALOGEN: _____

2. PACIFIC:OCEAN::COMEDY: _____

3. SUN:SOLAR SYSTEM::TRIBUTARY: _____

4. PROPELLER:PLANE::SMOKESTACK: _____

5. CHEF:RESTAURANT::DOCTOR: _____

Vocabulary Practice 22: Analogies

An **analogy** is a relationship between two pairs of words. In an analogy, the relationship between the first pair of words is the same as the relationship between the second pair of words.

A. Determine the relationship between the first pair of words. Write the word that completes the second pair of words in the analogy.

1. ASTUTE:OBTUSE::OPAQUE: _____
   a. brave   b. fuzzy   c. clear

2. BEFUDDLE:CLARIFY::METICULOUS: _____
   a. fastidious   b. sloppy   c. organized

3. CHASTE:PURE::DISCREET: _____
   a. secretive   b. obnoxious   c. disclosed

4. MUNDANE:ORDINARY::SPENDTHRIFT: _____
   a. investor   b. miser   c. squanderer

5. RECONCILIATION:PEACE::ANTIBIOTIC: _____
   a. infection   b. healing   c. pain

6. PRACTICE:PERFECTION::DISCIPLINE: _____
   a. order   b. anarchy   c. disbandment

7. NOURISHMENT:ENERGIZE::HUMOR: _____
   a. bore   b. disgust   c. amuse

8. EXERCISE:HEALTHINESS::REST: _____
   a. recuperation   b. sleep   c. exhaustion

9. SHIP:ARMADA::STAR: _____
   a. light   b. constellation   c. sun

10. SONNET:POEM::OREGANO: _____
    a. spice   b. pizza   c. Italian

B. Circle the letter of the word pair that completes each analogy.

1. SALT:PRESERVE:: _____
   a. teacher:instruct   b. book:read   c. ice cubes:melt

2. FRET:RELAX:: _____
   a. cultivate:destroy   b. lawyer:crime   c. coagulate:clump

3. OPTOMETRIST:PHYSICIAN:: _____
   a. walk:log   b. seaweed:ocean   c. acacia:tree

4. OBSCURE:KNOWN:: _____
   a. sedate:calm   b. frequent:seldom   c. vision:sight

5. EXPLORATION:DISCOVERY:: _____
   a. atmosphere:oxygen   b. tornadoes:havoc   c. raw:unexplored

Vocabulary Practice 23: Connotations and Denotations

A **connotation** is the implied or suggested meaning of a word or phrase. Words with similar meanings convey different connotations, depending on the text. The **denotation** of a word is the dictionary definition.

A. Using a dictionary, write the denotation of each word. Then, use the phrase in a sentence to illustrate the connotation of the word.

1. **bland** _____

   bland meal _____

2. **formal** _____

   formal wedding _____

3. **ignorant** _____

   ignorant of the law _____

4. **repetitious** _____

   repetitious message _____

5. **typical** _____

   typical response _____

6. **breathtaking** _____

   breathtaking scene _____

7. **defiant** _____

   defiant child _____

8. **innocuous** _____

   innocuous idea _____

9. **discreet** _____

   discreet meeting _____

10. **optimum** _____

    optimum performance _____

B. Use a dictionary or thesaurus to write two other words that are connotations for the bold-face words. Then, on other paper, write a sentence using one of the two words to convey its connotation.

1. **bland** _____	6. **breathtaking** _____
2. **formal** _____	7. **defiant** _____
3. **ignorant** _____	8. **innocuous** _____
4. **repetitious** _____	9. **discreet** _____
5. **typical** _____	10. **optimum** _____

Vocabulary Practice 24: Connotations and Denotations

A **connotation** is the implied or suggested meaning of a word or phrase. Words with similar meanings convey different connotations, depending on the text. The **denotation** of a word is the dictionary definition.

A. The denotation is given for each boldface word. Write the two words from the list that are connotations for the given word. Then, write a sentence using one of the words to convey its connotation.

consolidate	coax	indirect	appease	discriminating
apathetic	aspiring	unite	sensible	determined
settle	denounce	curb	seek	challenge
clever	confine	impel	unresponsive	stalk

1. **persuade** to cause to do something by reasoning or urging _____

_____

2. **subtle** making fine distinctions in meaning _____

_____

3. **indifferent** showing no partiality, bias, or preference _____

_____

4. **ambitious** striving, desirous, or eager for something _____

_____

_____

5. **sagacious** having or showing sound judgment or keen perception _____

_____

_____

6. **impugn** to oppose or attack by argument or criticism _____

_____

_____

7. **restrict** to put certain limits on _____

_____

8. **solidify** to make solid, firm, or strong _____

_____

9. **reconcile** to make friendly again or win over _____

_____

10. **pursue** to follow in order to overtake or to strive for _____

_____

B. On another piece of paper, write two more words that are connotations for each boldface word in Exercise A.

Name _____ Date _____

Vocabulary Practice 25: Connotations and Denotations

A **connotation** is the implied or suggested meaning of a word or phrase. It is different from the **denotation,** or dictionary definition. Connotations convey implied meanings—positive, neutral, or negative—depending on the text.

Example: The words *frugal* and *miserly* both mean "careful with money." *Frugal* describes a person who is thrifty or economical while *miserly* describes someone who is stingy or greedy. *Frugal* is a neutral implied meaning while *miserly* is a negative implied meaning.

A. Complete the sentences with two of the italicized words. Write a sentence using the third word to convey its connotation. Use a dictionary or thesaurus, if necessary.

1. Words that connote "ways of speaking one's opinion" are *candid, tactless,* and *complimentary.*

   a. Mitchell is _____ and sometimes offends sensitive people.

   b. Natalie is always _____ when asked her opinion about something.

   c. _____

2. Words that connote "repeated behavior" are *consistent, chronic,* and *habitual.*

   a. Nathan has a _____ cough so his mother takes him to the doctor frequently.

   b. Tom is _____ about paying bills on time and has a great credit rating.

   c. _____

3. Words that connote "a taste for style" are *old-fashioned, out-dated,* and *antique.*

   a. Each year we clean the closests and donate _____ clothing.

   b. Grandmother has a wonderful flair for everything _____ in her house.

   c. _____

4. Words that connote "degrees of asking for" are *request, plead,* and *demand.*

   a. A _____ is usually not the best way to achieve a desired goal.

   b. Children often _____ when asking parents for a special toy or privilege.

   c. _____

5. Words that connote "ways to look over" are *study, scrutinize,* and *observe.*

   a. On nature walks, we always _____ the birds, small animals, and insects.

   b. Seeing an empty nest, we _____ it to determine its former inhabitants.

   c. _____

B. On another piece of paper, write another word with the same meaning and a different connotation for the italicized words in Exercise A.

Vocabulary Practice 25: Connotations and Denotations   **25**

Name _____ Date _____

Vocabulary Practice 26: Commonly Misused Words

Having a good vocabulary means knowing the right word to use in speaking and writing. Many words are confused because they sound similar or their meanings are not understood.

Example: *Allusion* and *illusion* are often used incorrectly. *Allusion* means " a casual or indirect reference." *Illusion* means "a false idea or concept."

A. Write a brief definition for each boldface word, using a dictionary, if necessary.

1. **amount/number** _____

   _____

2. **berth/birth** _____

   _____

3. **older/elder** _____

   _____

4. **farther/further** _____

   _____

5. **personal/personnel** _____

   _____

6. **addition/edition** _____

   _____

7. **apathy/empathy** _____

   _____

8. **adapt/adopt** _____

   _____

9. **healthful/healthy** _____

   _____

10. **desert/dessert** _____

    _____

B. Complete each phrase with a word from Exercise A. Some words require suffixes. Then, on another piece of paper, write a sentence using the other word in each pair.

1. _____ siblings
2. _____ pet
3. _____ soups
4. _____ of people
5. fat-free _____

6. _____ for victims
7. walked _____
8. _____ of twins
9. _____ response
10. three-digit _____

Vocabulary Practice 27: Commonly Misused Words

Having a good vocabulary demands skillful use of the right words in speaking and writing. Many words sound alike and cause confusion when not understood.

A. Write a brief definition for each boldface word, using a dictionary, if necessary. Then, write the word that completes the sentence. Some words require suffixes.

1. **ability/capacity** _____

   Jane's new car has the _____ to be driven hundreds of miles on a tank of gasoline.

2. **advice/advise** _____

   Would _____ from an elderly person be appreciated by a very young person?

3. **affect/effect** _____

   Carnival events will not be _____ by a rainstorm unless there are high winds.

4. **aid/aide** _____

   At the hospital, the _____ are always busy visiting the infirmed to cheer them up.

5. **beside/besides** _____

   What should the children bring _____ cookies and cupcakes to the party?

6. **bring/take** _____

   "What will you _____ to dinner," Mathilde asked her sister.

7. **lose/loose** _____

   In hot weather, it's always a good idea to wear _____ clothing.

8. **site, sight, cite** _____

   Begin having your vision checked at an early age to avoid loss of _____.

9. **strait/straight** _____

   As we rounded the corner and went through the _____, we were hypnotized by the view.

10. **among/between** _____

    Confusion occurs unless it is remembered that the word _____ is used to compare two things.

B. On another piece of paper, write a sentence using each word not used in the sentences in Exercise A.

Vocabulary Practice 28: Commonly Misused Words

Many English words sound alike and cause confusion when not used correctly. Other words are confused in meaning and usage.

Example: The word *capital* and *capitol* sound alike, but have different spellings and meanings. *Capitol* with a capital *c* refers to the building in Washington, D.C., while *capital* means "principal" or "most important." The words *between* and *among* are often confused. *Between* compares two things; *among* compares three or more things.

A. Match the words and definitions. Write the letter of each definition before the word.

1. _____ unaware   a. to indicate indirectly

   _____ unawares   b. being part of the real nature of something

2. _____ accept   c. to struggle awkwardly in speaking or actions

   _____ except   d. to conclude or decide from something known

3. _____ eminent   e. not moving; fixed

   _____ imminent   f. to stumble, fall, or become stuck

4. _____ stationary   g. to avoid or escape unnoticed

   _____ stationery   h. to refer to in a casual way

5. _____ fewer than   i. not being part of or connected to something

   _____ less than   j. to omit or exclude

6. _____ allude   k. to put forward in opposition

   _____ elude   l. paper and envelopes

7. _____ imply   m. the lowest degree; miserable

   _____ infer   n. likely to happen soon

8. _____ flounder   o. to take or receive willingly

   _____ founder   p. refers to total or mass quantity

9. _____ abject   q. without knowing, unexpectedly

   _____ object   r. not aware conscious or/of

10. _____ extrinsic   s. rising above others, prominent

    _____ intrinsic   t. refers to the number of separate units of anything

B. Write the word that is used in each phrase. Then, on another piece of paper, write a phrase for the other words in Exercise A.

1. _____ to a secret   6. everyone _____ the decision

2. monogrammed _____   7. _____ in making a statement

3. _____ a quart but more than a pint   8. _____ or unimportant to the story

4. _____ thunderstorm   9. his _____ behavior

5. _____ a wrongdoing   10. caught _____

Vocabulary Practice 29: Commonly Misused Words Review

A. Use one word from each pair in the sentences.

addition/edition	further/farther	lose/loose
less than/fewer than	among/between	advice/advise
affect/effect	accept/except	amount/number
desert/dessert	imply/infer	stationary/stationery
adapt/adopt	eminent/imminent	beside/besides
coarse/course	minor/miner	later/latter
quiet/quite	formally/formerly	

1. Marge realized that she had not measured the _____ of sugar correctly.

2. The _____ speaker was internationally recognized and well respected.

3. _____ 1000 people filled the auditorium to vote on the stadium.

4. On _____ from his physician, the athlete sat out the games for the rest of the season.

5. Our dog could not _____ to the intrusion of the neighbors' dogs on his space.

6. We arrived home _____ than planned, never dreaming we were in for a surprise.

7. The presidential candidate will _____ the election without a majority of votes.

8. When the three friends met, they discussed who _____ them had lost the most weight.

9. Helen gets good exercise regularly by using her _____ bike.

10. The Capricorn Box Company was _____ owned by Mr. Quible's family.

11. The _____ all looked inviting so Jan decided to try the key lime pie.

12. Gasoline price increases will _____ summer travel plans.

13. Mother was _____ upset when the guests spilled drinks on her sofa.

14. The elderly woman became an instant celebrity when she walked _____ than anyone her age in a marathon.

15. Wildflowers grew _____ the steps with no care from the residents.

16. In the old bookstore, Anne found a rare _____ of her favorite book.

17. Students met with counselors to discuss their _____ .

18. Being a _____ means being underage and subject to age restrictions.

19. _____ for the book review, Ed had completed all his homework before dinner.

20. "What can you _____ from the character's behavior about his motives?" asked the teacher.

B. Write a sentence for five words not used in Exercise A.

Name _____   Date _____

Vocabulary Practice 30: Specialized Vocabulary

Having a basic understanding of legal terms helps when reading the newspaper, processing legal documents, and conversing about the law, among other purposes.

A. Match ten words and their definitions, using a dictionary, if necessary.

plaintiff	**deposition**	**perjury**	**libel**	**lien**
appellate court	**plagiarism**	**larceny**	**probate**	**defendant**
arraignment	**litigation**	**statute**	**subpoena**	**prosecutor**

_____ 1. the person who is filing a claim against someone

_____ 2. a court that reviews appeals

_____ 3. the willful telling of a lie while under lawful oath

_____ 4. the person being sued in a claim

_____ 5. the person who initiates lawsuit proceedings

_____ 6. a claim on another's property as security for debt payment

_____ 7. a lawsuit

_____ 8. appearance before a court of law to hear the charges in a lawsuit

_____ 9. a witness's testimony

_____ 10. an established rule

B. Write the definitions for the five remaining words.

1. _____

2. _____

3. _____

4. _____

5. _____

C. Look in a newspaper, magazine, legal document, or other source for an example of how each word or phrase in Exercise A is used. Then, write a sentence using each word or phrase. Include a reference to the source.

_____

_____

_____

_____

_____

_____

_____

_____

_____

_____

Vocabulary Practice 31: Specialized Vocabulary

Many English words are actually words derived or "borrowed" from other languages.

Example: The word *African* comes from the Latin word *Africa* meaning "land." Today, the word *African* is an adjective that describes the people, languages, and cultures of Africa. It is also a noun meaning "a native of the continent of Africa."

A. Match the words with their origins by writing the letter of the origin before the word that is used today. The list does not include all word origins.

1. _____ hurricane
2. _____ freight
3. _____ bravado
4. _____ gumbo
5. _____ mattress
6. _____ shampoo
7. _____ buoy
8. _____ chess
9. _____ pecan
10. _____ jungle

a. Hindi, *jangal,* "desert, forest"; Sanskrit, *jangala,* "dry ground"
b. Algerian, *paccan,* "nut of the hickory tree"; Native American, *pagan, pakan*
c. Arabic, *eschec* related to *shah,* "a king who controls the rules"
d. Spanish, *huracan;* Portuguese, *furacao;* Carribbean, *huracan,* "evil spirit of the sea"
e. Spanish, *bravada,* "a boast"; Italian, *bravata*
f. African-American, *ocingombo;* Angolan and Bantu, *kingombo,* "a stew made with okra"
g. Middle English, *frauht, fraucht,* "cargo"
h. Middle Dutch, *boeie,* Middle French, *boie* and *buie,* "a chain", or "held by a chain"
i. Middle English, Old French, *materas;* originally Arabic, *al-matrah,* "a place to put a mat"
j. Hindustani, *cchampo,* "a massage"; *shampna,* "giving a massage"

B. Write the word from Exercise A that matches each description of current use.

1. _____ now refers to a storm
2. _____ now means "a floating object anchored in a lake, river, or ocean to warn of a hazard"
3. _____ is an edible nut grown in the South
4. _____ is a kind of board game
5. _____ has derived to mean "brave"
6. _____ now means "to wash the scalp"
7. _____ now refers to objects carried by trucks, trains, and boats
8. _____ is a kind of dish native to a region
9. _____ is essentially the same word and spelling
10. _____ now means land overgrown with foliage

C. Use the dictionary to find ten more words borrowed from other languages. Write the words, their current meanings, and their origins.

Spelling Practice 1: Words With *ei* and *ie*

Words spelled with *ei* and *ie* follow rules for spelling with some exceptions.

Spelling Rule: Use *i* before *e* except after *c* or when sounded like *a* as in *neighbor* and *weigh*.

    Examples: The word *retrieve* and other words follow the *i* before *e* rule; words such as *receive* and *weird* are examples of "except after c." Other words such as *weight* are exceptions and must be learned. The rule applies only when *ei* or *ie* are in the same syllable. Thus words such as *be' ing* do not follow the rule.

A. Write these misspelled words correctly. Then, write the rule that applies to the spelling. Check your spelling in a dictionary. The first one is an example.

Spelling Word	Correct Spelling	Spelling Rule
1. casheir	cashier	i before e
2. conciet	_____	_____
3. riemburse	_____	_____
4. efficeint	_____	_____
5. caffiene	_____	_____
6. peity	_____	_____
7. deciet	_____	_____
8. concieve	_____	_____
9. speceis	_____	_____
10. impropreity	_____	_____
11. reciept	_____	_____
12. inviegh	_____	_____
13. yeild	_____	_____
14. breif	_____	_____
15. percieve	_____	_____
16. freind	_____	_____
17. gaeity	_____	_____
18. surviellance	_____	_____
19. beleif	_____	_____
20. vareity	_____	_____
21. shiek	_____	_____
22. retreive	_____	_____
23. sufficeint	_____	_____
24. anceint	_____	_____
25. feifdom	_____	_____

B. On other paper, add five more words that are exceptions to the rules.

Spelling Practice 2: Final e With Suffixes

When spelling words with final *e* and adding suffixes, follow rules for keeping or dropping *e*.

Spelling Rules

1. Drop the final silent *e* before a suffix that begins with a vowel.

 Examples: *close* and *-est* makes *closest; dine* and *-ing* makes *dining; use* and *-able* makes *usable*

2. Keep the final silent *e* in a word that ends in *ce* or *ge* before a suffix beginning with *a* or *o*.

 Examples: *changeable, courageous, mileage*

3. Keep the final silent *e* before a suffix that begins with a consonant.

 Examples: *grace* and *-ful* makes *graceful; amuse* and *-ment* makes *amusement*
 Exceptions: *judgment, acknowledgment, argument*

A. Add the suffixes to the words and write the new words. Write the number of the rule that applies to the spelling. Check your spelling in a dictionary.

	New Word	**Spelling Rule**
1. *arrange* and *ed* makes	_____	_____
2. *upgrade* and *ing* makes	_____	_____
3. *encourage* and *ment* makes	_____	_____
4. *hope* and *ful* makes	_____	_____
5. *nine* and *ty* makes	_____	_____
6. *service* and *able* makes	_____	_____
7. *erase* and *ed* makes	_____	_____
8. *taste* and *ful* makes	_____	_____
9. *advantage* and *ous* makes	_____	_____
10. *write* and *ing* makes	_____	_____

B. Underline the misspelled word in each sentence. Write the word correctly after the sentence.

1. Nell has acheived a great degree of success in playing her flute. _____

2. Since people have different skills and talents, compareing people isn't fair. _____

3. For the third time in one week, the actor has been late to the reherseal. _____

4. The jar cover was closed so tightly that it was not removeable. _____

5. Lee was remorsful about hurting her friend's feelings. _____

6. The two children had a loud arguement about which movie to see. _____

7. A safty law requires people to wear seatbelts in most states. _____

8. The restaurant prices were so outragous that we decided not to stay for dinner. _____

9. Our hamster is really thriveing on all the extra vitamins he's eating. _____

10. Often small children will strive hard in order to win their teacher's approval. _____

Name _____ Date _____

Spelling Practice 3: Final *y* With Suffixes

When spelling words with final *y* and adding suffixes, follow rules for keeping *y* or changing *y* to *i* before adding the suffix.

Spelling Rules

1. Change *y* to *i* when a consonant precedes *y*.

Examples: Adding *-es*, *-ed*, *-able*, or *-ing* to *deny* makes *denies*, *denied*, and *deniable*.
Exception: Adding *-ly* and *-ness* to *fussy* makes *fussily* and *fussiness*. *Denying* retains *y* before the suffix to avoid having two *i*'s.

2. Retain *y* when a vowel precedes *y*.

Example: Adding *-es*, *-ing*, *-ed* to *annoy* makes *annoys*, *annoying*, *annoyed*.

3. Retain *y* in one-syllable words before *-ly* and *-ness*.

Example: Adding *-ly* to *dry* makes *dryly* and *dryness*.
Exception: Adding *-ly* to *gay* makes *gaily*.

A. Add the suffixes *-es, -ed, -ing, -ly, -able,* or *-ness* and write the new words. Then, check your spelling in a dictionary.

Word With Suffix	**Word With Suffix**
1. *legacy* and *es* _____	16. *spry* and *ly* _____
2. *beautify* and *ing* _____	17. *scurry* and *ed* _____
3. *day* and *ly* _____	18. *spunky* and *ness* _____
4. *magnify* and *ed* _____	19. *liquefy* and *ed* _____
5. *employ* and *able* _____	20. *verify* and *able* _____
6. *tardy* and *ness* _____	21. *justify* and *ing* _____
7. *haughty* and *ly* _____	22. *hearty* and *ly* _____
8. *testify* and *ing* _____	23. *qualify* and *es* _____
9. *mystify* and *es* _____	24. *occupy* and *ing* _____
10. *cheery* and *ly* _____	25. *dizzy* and *ness* _____
11. *simplify* and *ed* _____	26. *memory* and *able* _____
12. *charity* and *able* _____	27. *uncanny* and *ly* _____
13. *heavy* and *ness* _____	28. *apology* and *es* _____
14. *fortify* and *ing* _____	29. *relay* and *ing* _____
15. *society* and *es* _____	30. *ally* and *ed* _____

B. Categorize the words you formed in Exercise A under the appropriate spelling rule. Begin on this page and complete the list on other paper.

Change *y* to *i*	**Retain *y***	**Exceptions**
_____	_____	_____
_____	_____	_____
_____	_____	_____
_____	_____	_____

Spelling Practice 4: Words Ending in *l* and *ll*

Words with sound-alike endings are often misspelled. Spelling rules help to spell words that end in *l* or *ll.*

Spelling Rules

1. Words with one syllable and a vowel before the final /l/ sound end in *ll* as in *call.*
2. Words with one syllable and two vowels before the final /l/ sound end in *l* as in *seal.*
3. Words with one syllable and a consonant before the final /l/ sound end in *l* as in *crawl.*
4. Words with two or more syllables may end in *l* as in *special* or in *ll* as in *treadmill.*

A. Add *l* or *ll* to these words.

1. fri _____
2. concea _____
3. vertica _____
4. appea _____
5. theatrica _____
6. rea _____
7. whir _____
8. chlorophy _____
9. spraw _____
10. disma _____

11. thri _____
12. repea _____
13. shaw _____
14. Brazi _____
15. qui _____
16. knee _____
17. snar _____
18. goodwi _____
19. whippoorwi _____
20. daffodi _____

B. Write the words in Exercise A under the appropriate spelling rule. The examples are a guide. Then, add five more words to each list.

Rule 1/*call*	Rule 2/*seal*	Rule 3/*crawl*	Rule 4/*special/treadmill*
_____	_____	_____	_____
_____	_____	_____	_____
_____	_____	_____	_____
_____	_____	_____	_____
_____	_____	_____	_____
_____	_____	_____	_____
_____	_____	_____	_____
_____	_____	_____	_____
_____	_____	_____	_____
_____	_____	_____	_____
_____	_____	_____	_____
_____	_____	_____	_____
_____	_____	_____	_____

Spelling Practice 5: Double the Final Consonant

When adding suffixes to words with a final consonant and a consonant-vowel-consonant (c-v-c) pattern, follow the rules for doubling the final consonant. In most words that do not follow the c-v-c pattern, the final consonant is not doubled when adding a suffix.

Spelling Rules

1. In one-syllable words that end in a c-v-c pattern, double the final consonant when adding a suffix beginning with a vowel, but not when adding a suffix beginning with a consonant.

   Example: The word *top* is one syllable with the c-v-c pattern. When adding *-ed* or *-ing*, double the final consonant and add the suffix to make *topped* or *topping*. When adding *-ly* or *-ness*, do not double the final consonant, as in *slowly* and *slowness*.

2. In words with two or more syllables that end in a c-v-c pattern and a stressed last syllable, double the final consonant when adding a suffix that begins with a vowel, but not when the suffix begins with a consonant. Do not double the final consonant if the last syllable is not stressed.

   Example: The word *control* ends in a c-v-c pattern (*control*) and the last syllable is stressed. When adding *-ing*, double the final consonant, as in *controlling*.

3. In words that end with two or more consonants, do not double the final consonant when adding a suffix.

   Example: The word *round* has two ending consonants. Adding *-ed* or *-ing* to *round* makes *rounded* and *rounding*.

4. Certain letters are never doubled before adding a suffix: *c, h, j, k, v, w, x,* and *y*.

   Examples: *mower, fixed, swayed*

A. Add the suffixes to the words and write the new words. Write the number of the spelling rule that applies.

Word with Suffix	Spelling Rule		Word with Suffix	Spelling Rule
1. *relax* and *ed* _____	____	11. *moral* and *ly* _____	____
2. *grin* and *ing* _____	____	12. *appoint* and *ment* _____	____
3. *accidental* and *ly* _____	____	13. *shy* and *ness* _____	____
4. *commit* and *ment* _____	____	14. *parallel* and *ing* _____	____
5. *retract* and *able* _____	____	15. *permit* and *ed* _____	____
6. *candid* and *ness* _____	____	16. *patrol* and *er* _____	____
7. *expound* and *ed* _____	____	17. *propel* and *ing* _____	____
8. *plan* and *ed* _____	____	18. *literal* and *ly* _____	____
9. *import* and *er* _____	____	19. *thick* and *ly* _____	____
10. *submit* and *ed* _____	____	20. *entrap* and *ment* _____	____

Spelling Practice 5: Double the Final Consonant

B. Determine whether or not each word is spelled correctly. If spelled correctly, put a check beside the word. Write the misspelled words correctly.

1. disjointted _____
2. beginner _____
3. discoverring _____
4. clotted _____
5. benefitting _____
6. overcommited _____
7. enrichment _____
8. stackking _____
9. contenttment _____
10. confidently _____
11. loyaly _____
12. flowwing _____
13. wraped _____
14. extractt _____
15. sounddness _____

16. rationaly _____
17. cancelled _____
18. traveller _____
19. commenddable _____
20. forgetfullness _____
21. objectted _____
22. repelent _____
23. remarkable _____
24. correcttness _____
25. taxing _____
26. transfering _____
27. amenddment _____
28. renewwed _____
29. squawkking _____
30. regrettable _____

C. Organize the words for doubling the final consonant in Exercise B, using the spelling rules on page 36.

Spelling Rule 1	Spelling Rule 2	Spelling Rule 3	Spelling Rule 4
_____	_____	_____	_____
_____	_____	_____	_____
_____	_____	_____	_____
_____	_____	_____	_____
_____	_____	_____	_____
_____	_____	_____	_____
_____	_____	_____	_____
_____	_____	_____	_____
_____	_____	_____	_____
_____	_____	_____	_____

D. Add five more words to each spelling rule.

1. _____ _____ _____ _____
2. _____ _____ _____ _____
3. _____ _____ _____ _____
4. _____ _____ _____ _____
5. _____ _____ _____ _____

Spelling Practice 6: Words Ending in -cede, -ceed, -sede

Words with sound-alike endings are often misspelled. Some words follow spelling rules. Other words such as those with the endings *–cede, -ceed,* and *–sede* must be learned. Three words end in *–ceed* and one word ends in *–sede.* All other words are spelled *-cede.*

A. Add the word endings to complete the words. Then, write the definitions of the words. Use a dictionary, if necessary.

-cede	**-ceed**	**-sede**

1. pre _____   4. se _____   7. pro _____   10. super _____

2. re _____   5. ac _____   8. suc _____

3. inter _____   6. con _____   9. ex _____

1. _____

2. _____

3. _____

4. _____

5. _____

6. _____

7. _____

8. _____

9. _____

10. _____

B. Write the words from Exercise A in the sentences. Some words require suffixes.

1. The Secretary of State was asked to _____ in negotiations to resolve the conflict.

2. Three countries _____ to a treaty to bring peace to the region.

3. Our teacher said that the class's SAT scores _____ her expectations.

4. Once the driver received directions, the bus _____ to the village.

5. At low tide, it's great to watch the ocean _____ from the shore.

6. The new credit card contract _____ the earlier one.

7. The tennis player _____ that the challenger had a better serve.

8. During the Civil War, the southern states decided to _____ from the Union.

9. A new convenience store opened, but did not _____ here.

10. If Jack _____ me in arriving at the concert, he will buy the tickets.

Spelling Practice 7: Words Ending in *-el* and *-le*

Words that end in *-el* and *-le* sound alike and are often misspelled. While most words are spelled *-le*, spelling rules help to remember and spell these words correctly.

Spelling Rules
1. Words with the letters *m, n, r, v,* and *w* are followed by *-el* as in *enamel* and *quarrel.*

2. The letter *c* with the /s/ sound and the letter *g* with the /j/ sound are followed by *-el* as in *cancel* and *angel.*

3. The letters *b, d, f, g, p,* and *t* are followed by *-le* as in *ladle, dangle,* and *mingle.*
   Exceptions: *bagel, mantel, label, model, scalpel*

4. The sounds /k/ and /z/ are followed by *-le* as in *sizzle* and *fickle.*
   Exceptions: *nickel, hazel*

A. Determine whether or not each word is spelled correctly. If spelled correctly, put a check (√) beside the word. Write the misspelled words correctly.

1. pinnacel _____	16. sorrle _____
2. humbel _____	17. crippel _____
3. monocel _____	18. vehicel _____
4. fizzel _____	19. whistel _____
5. parcle _____	20. barrle _____
6. squirrle _____	21. subtel _____
7. rippel _____	22. hazle _____
8. principel _____	23. libel _____
9. hobbel _____	24. trickel _____
10. trouble _____	25. chapel _____
11. icicel _____	26. hostle _____
12. noble _____	27. duffel _____
13. frazzel _____	28. spectacel _____
14. minstrel _____	29. trembel _____
15. marvle _____	30. triangel _____

B. Write the words from Exercise A under the appropriate spelling rule. You will need another piece of paper.

Rule 1	Rule 2	Rule 3	Rule 4
_____	_____	_____	_____
_____	_____	_____	_____
_____	_____	_____	_____
_____	_____	_____	_____
_____	_____	_____	_____
_____	_____	_____	_____
_____	_____	_____	_____

Spelling Practice 7: Words Ending in *-el* and *-le*

C. For each boldface word, write the number of the spelling rule on page 39 that applies to the word. Then write two words from the list that follow the same spelling rule or that are exceptions.

trowel	cradle	fiddle	fizzle	hostel
marvel	parcel	novel	shingle	sorrel
snorkel	simple	tangle	squirrel	tinsel
trickle	trample	tackle	panel	throttle
grapple	maple	nibble	pummel	waffle
propel	ripple	assemble	brittle	cancel

Word	**Spelling Rule**	**Two Words and Exceptions for the Same Rule**
1. **bangle**	_____	_____ _____
2. **chancel**	_____	_____ _____
3. **ignoble**	_____	_____ _____
4. **thistle**	_____	_____ _____
5. **scalpel**	_____	_____ _____
6. **throttle**	_____	_____ _____
7. **wrangle**	_____	_____ _____
8. **swivel**	_____	_____ _____
9. **travel**	_____	_____ _____
10. **muffle**	_____	_____ _____
11. **flannel**	_____	_____ _____
12. **funnel**	_____	_____ _____
13. **pickle**	_____	_____ _____
14. **circle**	_____	_____ _____
15. **mingle**	_____	_____ _____

D. Choose one word from Exercise C that follows each spelling rule and exception. Write a sentence using each word and underline it.

_____

_____

_____

_____

_____

_____

_____

_____

_____

_____

_____

Spelling Practice 8: Words Ending in *-er* and *-re*

Most words in English are spelled with the ending *-er*, but a few words are spelled with the ending *-re*, using the British spelling.

A. Write the ending *-er* or *-re* to complete each word. Check your spelling in a dictionary.

1. conf _____
2. farth _____
3. theat _____
4. charact _____
5. sequest _____
6. ling _____
7. meag _____
8. cloist _____
9. ac _____
10. engend _____
11. zith _____
12. should _____
13. leath _____
14. trail _____
15. macab _____
16. deciph _____
17. toddl _____
18. ref _____
19. medioc _____
20. philosoph _____
21. meand _____
22. og _____
23. massac _____
24. marin _____
25. gen _____
26. feath _____
27. timb _____
28. cent _____
29. answ _____
30. photograph _____

B. Write the words that are spelled two ways, with *-er* and *-re*.

_____   _____
_____   _____
_____   _____
_____   _____
_____   _____

C. Write a word ending in *-er* or *-re* to complete each phrase. Use the words in Exercise A or your own.

1. _____ handbag
2. story _____
3. wedding _____
4. mischievous _____
5. tales by a _____
6. _____ a code
7. _____ movie
8. literary _____
9. _____ of corn
10. village _____

Name _____ Date _____

Spelling Practice 9: Commonly Misspelled Words

Words with single or double medial consonant letters are often misspelled. There are no spelling rules for words with medial consonant letters. Words that are spelled the same except for the medial consonant have different meanings.

Example: The word *caned* means made with cane as a chair, while *canned* means "preserved in a jar or can."

A. Write the correct spelling of each word with a double medial consonant. Put a check (√) beside words with a single medial consonant.

1. abreviate _____	16. ocasion _____
2. acidentally _____	17. paralel _____
3. acumulate _____	18. posess _____
4. buletin _____	19. suceed _____
5. comittee _____	20. hoping _____
6. planing _____	21. sylable _____
7. scisors _____	22. tomorow _____
8. embarass _____	23. vilain _____
9. taped _____	24. griper _____
10. exagerate _____	25. mating _____
11. gramar _____	26. striped _____
12. imigrant _____	27. regretable _____
13. mispell _____	28. corespondence _____
14. riper _____	29. reference _____
15. disapoint _____	30. flanel _____

B. List the words in Exercise A that are spelled correctly with a single medial consonant. Then, write the same words with double medial consonants. On a separate page, write the definitions of both words, using a dictionary, if necessary.

Words with Single Medial Consonants	**Words with Double Medial Consonants**
1. _____	_____
2. _____	_____
3. _____	_____
4. _____	_____
5. _____	_____
6. _____	_____
7. _____	_____

Spelling Practice 10: Commonly Misspelled Words

Words spelled with two or three medial vowels such as *ea, ie, ai, eo, ei, ou,* and *iou* are frequently misspelled.

A. Determine whether or not each word is spelled correctly. Write the misspelled words correctly. Put a check (√) beside the words that are spelled correctly.

1. acheeve _____
2. aireal _____
3. aisle _____
4. anxiaty _____
5. approach _____
6. turmiol _____
7. hieght _____
8. despaer _____
9. aighth _____
10. forign _____
11. appeese _____
12. bemone _____
13. aviary _____
14. amphibious _____
15. belaeguer _____

16. assauge _____
17. boysterous _____
18. prosaic _____
19. variaty _____
20. cheeper _____
21. glamoruos _____
22. recieving _____
23. ingenoius _____
24. cloyster _____
25. copius _____
26. dissaude _____
27. nieve _____
28. pliable _____
29. furoius _____
30. infamous _____

B. For each set of medial vowels, write two words from Exercise A with the same medial vowels.

1. *ei* _____   _____
2. *ie* _____   _____
3. *ai* _____   _____
4. *ia* _____   _____
5. *ee* _____   _____
6. *ea* _____   _____
7. *oa* _____   _____
8. *oi* _____   _____
9. *ou* _____   _____
10. *iou* _____   _____

Name _____ Date _____

Spelling Practice Review

A. Write the misspelled words correctly. Put a check (√) beside the words that are spelled correctly.

1. abreviate _____
2. embarass _____
3. enamal _____
4. exaggerrate _____
5. conifur _____
6. paralell _____
7. beautifing _____
8. posesses _____
9. dissapoint _____
10. grammar _____
11. commitee _____
12. mispell _____
13. ambivalance _____
14. benevolance _____
15. tardyness _____
16. independence _____
17. nuisence _____
18. resistence _____
19. admitance _____
20. acquaintence _____
21. attendence _____
22. spectacal _____
23. aireal _____
24. consience _____
25. simplyfied _____
26. grief _____
27. occassion _____
28. referance _____
29. sylable _____
30. linger _____
31. acheive _____
32. liquefy _____
33. imigrant _____
34. allowence _____
35. anxeity _____
36. annoyed _____
37. judgemental _____
38. resonence _____
39. vareity _____
40. charactre _____
41. hindrence _____
42. delinate _____
43. impervous _____
44. compel _____
45. sucede _____
46. divergance _____
47. foreign _____
48. accidentaly _____
49. arguementative _____
50. circutious _____
51. scalpel _____
52. sagaceous _____
53. naieve _____
54. acknowledgement _____
55. unweildy _____
56. precede _____
57. gentele _____
58. discrete _____
59. phrophecy _____
60. fallibel _____

B. On a separate page, organize all the words in Exercise A according to the spelling rule that applies. Include the exceptions to the rules. Briefly state the spelling rules.

ANSWERS

ANSWERS

Vocabulary Practice 1: Prefixes (p. 1)

A. 1. extraterrestrial: "beyond the earth"

2. interplanetary: "between the planets"

3. intraocular: "within the eye"

4. ultrasound: "beyond or exceeding human hearing"

5. introspection: "examining inward"

6. extracurricular: "beyond courses of study"

7. interdependent: "dependent on each other"

8. intravenous: "within the veins"

9. ultramodernist: "one who exceeds (or is extreme) in current views"

10. introversion: "turning inward" (to the self)

B. (Sentences are sample responses.)

1. extraordinary: We enjoyed an extraordinary dinner prepared by a master chef.

2. extrasensory: The movie effects gave us an extrasensory experience.

3. extraterritorial: Extraterritorial rights were extended by the government.

4. intercollegiate: Our soccer team is participating in the intercollegiate games.

5. interdisciplinary: History and literature are being taught in an interdisciplinary approach.

6. intercultural: We had a huge intercultural party in our town.

7. intramural: My brother plays intramural sports.

8. intramuscular: The doctor performed intramuscular tests on my arm.

9. intrados: The architect drew the intrados with a design.

10. ultraviolet: Ultraviolet light is used in radiation.

11. ultraconservative: My grandad who experienced the Depression is ultraconservative.

12. ultrasound: Doctors depend on ultrasound for diagnosis.

13. introduce: The teacher introduced the new student to the class.

14. introvert: Someone who is an introvert is quiet and shy around others.

15. introductory: An introductory offer to join the health club was a great deal.

Vocabulary Practice 2: Prefixes (p. 2)

A. 1. a. Sample answer

b. forecast: "to estimate in advance"

c. foreshadow: "to show or indicate beforehand"

2. a. antedate: "to put on a date that is before the actual date"

b. antechamber: "a small room in front of a larger room"

c. antemortem: "made or done just before one's death"

3. a. prearrange: "to arrange prior to another event or situation"

b. premature: "happening or existing prior to the proper or usual time"

c. prejudge: "to judge prior to having all the evidence"

4. a. proclaim: "to announce officially or in favor of"

b. proactive: "moving forward or taking action"

c. prolong: "to extend time forward or lengthen"

5. a. postmillenial: "existing or happening after the millenium"

b. postgraduate: "after graduation, or after receipt of a bachelor's degree"

c. postoperative: "occurring after a surgical operation"

B. 1. proactive

2. antechamber

3. postmillenial

4. premature

5. foreshadow

Vocabulary Practice 3: Prefixes (p. 3)

A. 1. allergic

2. satisfactory

3. appropriate

4. typical

5. harmonious
6. warranted
7. restricted
8. informed
9. symmetrical
10. hospitable

B.

	non-	un-	in-	a-
1.	athletic	formulated	capacitate	morphous
2.	compliance	impeded	gratitude	pathy (pathos)
3.	flammable	licensed	humane	pteryx (wings)
4.	professional	obtrusive	sensitive	pyretic (fever)
5.	transferable	questionable	tangible	symptomatic

C. 1. *unreliable* means "cannot be counted upon"
2. *nonspecific* means "not limiting or limited"
3. *amoral* means "without moral sense or principles"
4. *indelicate* means "not sensitive, discriminating, or refined"

Vocabulary Practice 4: Prefixes (p. 4)

A. 1. monaural
2. unicorn
3. monotone
4. monorail
5. monogamy
6. universal
7. monarchy
8. uniform
9. monolingual
10. unilateral

B. 1. mono tone
2. mono rail
3. mono gamy
4. mon archy
5. uni versal
6. mono lingual
7. uni corn
8. uni form
9. mono aural
10. uni lateral

C. 1. *monograph* means "a book or long article on a single subject"
2. *monochromatic* means "having one color"
3. *monaxial* means "having one axis"
4. *monanthous* means "having one flower"
5. *unison* means "an interval of two identical musical pitches; harmony; agreement"
6. *unipolar* means "having one magnetic or electrical pole"

Vocabulary Practice 5: Suffixes (p. 5)

A. 1. Sample Answer
2. defend   -ant   8
3. conduct   -or   13
4. special   -ist   6
5. design   -er   15
6. orate   -or   4
7. machine   -ist   14
8. employ   -er   10
9. account   -ant   12
10. column   -ist   1
11. legislate   -or   7
12. final   -ist   9
13. arbitrate   -or   2
14. assist   -ant   3
15. schol   -ar   11

B.

	-ist	*-ant*	*-or*	*-er*	*-ar*
1.	altruist	applicant	administrator	cartographer	beggar
2.	archivist	debutant	editor	debater	commissar
3.	botanist	immigrant	innovator	skater	consular
4.	protagonist	merchant	perpetrator	teacher	registrar
5.	scientist	truant	tenor	writer	tutelar

Vocabulary Practice 6: Suffixes (p. 6)

A.
1. -ic electronic
2. -ic optimistic
3. -ic fantastic
4. -ile projectile
5. -ive supportive
6. -ile fragile
7. -ive selective
8. -ive successive
9. -ic magnetic
10. -ic tactic

B.
1. magnetic
2. electronic
3. supportive
4. selective
5. projectile
6. fragile
7. optimistic
8. tactic

C. (Sample response)

Nigel and his grandfather decided to find out how rockets are launched at the Kennedy Space Center. They went to the library. Of course, they couldn't reproduce a real launch pad, but they got ideas from reading. Together, they created new launch pads and tried them out.

With each successful trial, the rocket made a better launch. Finally, the rocket made a perfect launch. It was a fantastic success for Nigel and his grandfather!

Vocabulary Practice 7: Suffixes (p. 7)

A.
1. brotherhood	1. awkwardness	1. individuality
2. neighborhood	2. likeness	2. activity
3. parenthood	3. responsiveness	3. curiosity
4. childhood	4. friendliness	4. rapidity
5. statehood	5. astuteness	5. originality

B.
1. parenthood
2. originality
3. likeness
4. curiosity
5. responsiveness
6. statehood
7. rapidity
8. friendliness
9. childhood
10. astuteness

Vocabulary Practice 8: Suffixes (p. 8)

A.
1. commencement
2. expression
3. disagreement
4. conclusion
5. concentration
6. commitment
7. juxtaposition
8. diplomacy
9. enrichment
10. normalcy

B.
1. enrichment
2. normalcy
3. concentration
4. juxtaposition
5. disagreement
6. expression
7. commencement
8. commitment
9. conclusion
10. diplomacy

C.
-ion, -sion, or -tion	-ment	-cy
2. express	1. commence	8. diplomat
4. conclude	3. disagree	10. normal
5. concentrate	6. commit	
7. juxtapose	9. enrich	

Vocabulary Practice 9: Word Roots (p. 9)

A.
spec	vis	vis	vis	scope
spec	scop	vid	spect	scope

B.
1. *periscope* means "an optical instrument that provides a clear lateral or oblique range of view"
2. *spectrum* means "the series of colored bands arranged in order of respective wavelengths"
3. *circumspect* means "careful to consider all circumstances before acting or deciding"
4. *kaleidoscope* means "a tubular instrument containing pieces of loose glass with mirrors that reflect symmetrical patterns when the tube is rotated"
5. *visionary* means "a person with acuteness or keen foresight with the power of imagination"

6. *gyroscope* means "a wheel mounted in a set of rings so that its axis of rotation can turn in any direction"

7. *specimen* means "a part of a whole used as an example of the whole"

8. *evidence* means "something that tends to prove"

9. *improvise* means "to compose and/or simultaneously perform, without preparation"

10. *seismoscope* means "an instrument that indicates the time and occurrence of earthquakes"

Vocabulary Practice 10: Word Roots (p. 10)

A. 1. sensible; tang, tact, sens

2. sensitive; sens, pass, tact

3. intangible; path, path, tang

4. compassion; tact, pass, sens

5. tangible; tang, sens, pass

6. intact; tact, path, tact

7. sentiment; sens, sent, tact

8. impassioned; path, pass, tang

9. tangential; tang, pass, sent

10. tactic; sens, tact, path

B. Sample answers.

1. The word *sensible* is the answer because the root -sens- means "think," and *sensible* means "showing good sense or judgment"

3. The word *intangible* is the answer because the root -tang- means "touch," and *intangible* means "that cannot be touched"

4. The word *compassion* is the answer because the root -pass- means "feel," and *compassion* means "sorrow for the sufferings of others"

Vocabulary Practice 11: Word Roots (p. 11)

A. resolve, solvable, solute, dissolved, solution, solvents, soluble, solved, absolve, solution

B. 1. solvents

2. resolve

3. solved

4. soluble

5. dissolved

6. absolve

7. solution

8. solvable

9. solution

10. solute

C. (Sample response)

Dr. Distraction had written the combinations of the solvents and labeled them A, B, C. When he reviewed the combinations, he remembered that one solvent doubles in impact when combined with another solvent. The effect is that the solution turns blue. Dr. Distraction wrote the formula for the solution that worked and put it in a safe place. He would not mix the wrong solvents again!

Vocabulary Practice 12: Word Roots (p. 12)

A. 1. *protocol* means "an original draft of a document"

2. *primitive* means "of or existing in the beginning or the earliest times or ages"

3. *prototype* means "the first of its kind; a model or pattern"

4. *protagonist* means "the main character in a drama, novel, or story"

5. *protein* means "any of a large class of nitrogenous substances occurring in all animal and vegetable matter, essential to the diet of animals"

6. *prime meridian* means "the imaginary line at 0° longitude, passing through Greenwich, England"

7. *primary* means "first in importance; chief; main"

8. *principle* means "first in rank, authority, or importance"

9. *primatologist* means "one who studies the branch of zoology dealing with primates"

10. *primogeniture* means "the fact of being the firstborn of the same parents"

B. 1. *primordial* means "first in time"

2. *primate* means "any of an order of mammal, including humans, apes, monkeys, and lemurs"

3. *primacy* means "the state of being first in time, order, rank"

4. *protoplast* means "a thing or being that is the first of its kind"

5. *protohistory* means "archeological history in the period immediately preceding recorded history"

Vocabulary Practice 13: Word Roots (p. 13)

A. 1. status: position
2. instability: unevenness
3. stationary: standing
4. ecstatic: overjoyed
5. stature: importance
6. established: declared
7. stabilize: balance
8. statistics: data
9. stagnant: motionless
10. stance: pose

B. (Sentences are sample responses.)
1. The school has standards for prompt arrival at 8:15 AM and departure from the school at 2:00 PM.
2. In our state, the statute governing a driver's license is a minimum age of 16 years.
3. An electrician might use a rheostat.
4. A stable environment means regular exercise, a good diet, and lots of love.
5. If a pond stagnates, the water is unfit for fish and other life.

Vocabulary Practice 14: Synonyms (p. 14)

A. 1. legacy   6. waver
2. endurance   7. focused
3. articulate   8. suffice
4. perpetuate   9. pursue
5. astute   10. naïve

B. 1. naïve
2. waver
3. focused
4. articulate
5. perpetuate
6. endurance
7. legacy
8. pursue
9. astute
10. suffice

C. 1. commitment: obligation, responsibility, duty
2. inherited: received, acquired, get
3. options: choices, selections, elections

D. The word *articulate* means "expressing oneself easily and clearly."

Vocabulary Practice 15: Synonyms (p. 15)

A. 1. befuddle
2. blithe
3. circuitous
4. coagulate
5. foible
6. opaque
7. raze
8. opulent
9. reconciliation
10. rudimentary

B. 1. rudimentary
2. raze
3. opaque
4. reconciliation
5. circuitous
6. opulent
7. coagulate
8. blithe
9. foible
10. befuddle

C. 1. circuitous: indirect, roundabout, meandering, oblique, rambling, winding
2. blithe: carefree, cheerful, frisky, gay, happy, jolly, joyful
3. rudimentary: basic, elementary, early, first, fundamental, immature, initial, introductory, primary, primative, undeveloped
4. opaque: blurred, clouded, dark, dim, impenetrable, impermeable, murky, obfuscated
5. foible: defect, failing, flaw, fault, blemish, imperfection, shortcoming, weakness

Vocabulary Practice 16: Synonyms (p. 16)

A. 1. c 2. a 3. b 4. c 5. c 6. b 7. c 8. a 9. b 10. a

B. 1. timely
2. objectionable
3. cultured
4. acknowledge
5. bemoan

Vocabulary Practice 17: Antonyms (p. 17)

A. 1. subtle
2. defiant

3. reject
4. sullen
5. judicious
6. literal
7. mute
8. genteel
9. introspective
10. alien

B. (Sentence completions are sample responses.)

1. mute; the emcee called upon her for the answer
2. defiant; whispered a surprise treat later if she behaved
3. introspective; blushing and becoming tongue-tied
4. sullen; saw the doctor open the medicine cabinet
5. judicious; explained their responsibilities as jurors

Vocabulary Practice 18: Antonyms (p. 18)

A. 1. neglected
2. crass
3. spurn
4. commence
5. ravenous
6. placid
7. verbose
8. discreet
9. dishearten
10. chaste

B. 1. neglected: attended to, remembered, heeded, considered
2. commence: end, stop, finish, complete, close, terminate
3. discreet: free, open, unconcealed, overt, exposed, known
4. verbose: concise, succinct, terse, pithy, curt
5. placid: disturbed, unsettled, troubled, agitated, turbulent, tumultuous

Vocabulary Practice 19: Antonyms (p. 19)

A. 1. b 2. c 3. b 4. b 5. c 6. b 7. a 8. a 9. b 10. a

B. 1. original
2. plump

3. commence
4. humble
5. deny

Vocabulary Practice 20: Synonym and Antonym Review (p. 20)

A. 1. b 2. d 3. a 4. c 5. a 6. d 7. a 8. d
B. 1. a 2. c 3. d 4. b 5. d 6. c 7. b 8. d
C. 1. *opaque*   syn: impenetrable
                      ant: transparent
     2. *defiant*   syn: disobedient
                      ant: respectful
     3. *dishearten* syn: discourage
                      ant: cheer up
     4. *naïve*   syn: innocent
                      ant: worldly

Vocabulary Practice 21: Analogies (p. 21)

A. 1. c 2. e 3. a 4. c 5. c 6. e 7. d 8. c 9. c 10. b
B. 1. lamp
2. movie
3. river
4. steamship
5. hospital

Vocabulary Practice 22: Analogies (p. 22)

A. 1. clear
2. sloppy
3. secretive
4. squanderer
5. healing
6. order
7. amuse
8. recuperation
9. constellation
10. spice
B. 1. a 2. a 3. c 4. b 5. b

Vocabulary Practice 23: Connotations and Denotations (p. 23)

A. (Sentences are sample responses.)

1. tasteless; insipid, dull
   Cousin Edna cooked a bland meal of boiled meat and potatoes.
2. of or according to prescribed or fixed customs, rules, ceremonies
   We attended a formal wedding and enjoyed sharing in the traditions.

3. having little knowledge, education or experience

   The policeman who stopped my car did not accept my excuse of being *ignorant* of the law.

4. full of or characterized by doing or saying again and again.

   The business I called had a *repetitious* message.

5. serving as a type; of or belonging to a representative example

   A *typical* response to the customer was "we are out of stock."

6. taking one's breath away; very exciting or thrilling

   We stopped the car to get out and enjoy a *breathtaking* scene.

7. openly and boldly resisting

   The teacher calmed the *defiant* child by playing a game.

8. not controversial, offensive, or stimulating

   One tourist's *innocuous* idea proved valuable for the group.

9. careful about what one says or does

   Managers held a *discreet* meeting to plan promotions.

10. the best or most favorable degree, condition, amount

    The car's *optimum* performance was achieved after servicing.

B. (Sentences are sample responses.)

1. flavorless, insipid

   Molly's stew was *flavorless.*

2. affected, precise

   The test questions are *precise.*

3. crass, illiterate

   Illiterate children were taught to read.

4. restated, imitated

   The child *imitated* his Dad's walk.

5. average, commonplace

   Holiday greetings are often *commonplace.*

6. magnificent, impressive

   We enjoyed an *impressive* exhibition of folk art.

7. disobedient, hostile

   Some *hostile* visitors were escorted to the exit.

8. harmless, unobjectionable

   Rules were *unobjectionable,* though inconvenient for visitors.

9. cautious, reserved

   Sally was *cautious* when responding to her friend's comments about her own weight gain.

10. best, unsurpassed

    We found the quality of the service *unsurpassed* at the new hotel.

Vocabulary Practice 24: Connotations and Denotations (p. 24)

A. (Sentences are sample responses.)

1. coax, impel

   Maria coaxed her puppy to come away from the street.

2. indirect, discriminating

   The campaign used indirect language to lure voters.

3. apathetic, unresponsive

   Voters were unresponsive to the new candidate.

4. aspiring, determined

   Employees are determined to have an exercise room.

5. clever, sensible

   Jake was sensible and cautious when using his Dad's car.

6. denounce, challenge

   Opposing sides challenged the budget for a new athletic field.

7. confine, curb

   Some of the parents have curbed weekend parties.

8. consolidate, unite

   Two small companies will consolidate their manufacturing units.

9. settle, appease

   Disputing neighbors settled their differences.

10. seek, stalk

    A resident is seeking a change in the local tax laws.

B. 1. *persuade*: convince, talk into

   2. *subtle*: delicate, refined

   3. *indifferent*: disinterested, objective

   4. *ambitious*: assertive, demanding

5. *sagacious*: astute, shrewd

6. *impugn*: oppose, attack

7. *restrict*: contain, impede

8. *solidify*: compress, unify

9. *reconcile*: pacify, harmonize

10. *pursue*: follow, cultivate

Vocabulary Practice 25: Connotations and Denotations (p. 25)

A. (Sentences are sample responses.)

1. a. tactless
   b. candid/complimentary
   c. A person's *candid*, or honest response is not always positive.

   A person's *complimentary* response is usually appreciated.

2. a. chronic
   b. consistent
   c. Ally's *habitual* tardiness earned her detention.

3. a. outdated
   b. antique
   c. Grandad is *old-fashioned* in his cash-only method of making purchases.

4. a. demand
   b. plead
   c. Our librarian issued a *request* to return overdue books.

5. a. study
   b. scrutinize
   c. On the trail, we *observe* birds unfamiliar to most of us.

B. 1. honest
   2. regular
   3. obsolete
   4. insist on
   5. contemplate

Vocabulary Practice 26: Commonly Misused Words (p. 26)

A. 1. *amount* means "the sum of two or more quantities" and refers to bulk items

   number means "the sum or total of persons or units" and refers to separate units

2. *berth* means "a space for tying up a ship; a compartment"

   birth means "the process of coming into life"

3. *older* means "having lived for a longer time"

   elder means "exceeding another in age"

4. *farther* means "more distant or remote"

   further means "to a greater degree or extent"

5. *personal* means "private; individual"

   personnel means "persons employed in any work, service, or establishment"

6. *addition* means "an adding of two or more numbers to get a sum"

   edition means "the size, style, or form in which a book is published"

7. *apathy* means "lack of emotion"

   empathy means "the projection of one's personality into another's to understand the person better"

8. *adapt* means "to make suitable by changing or adjusting"

   adopt means "to choose and bring into a certain relationship by legal process"

9. *healthful* means "helping to produce, promote, or maintain health"

   healthy means "having good health"

10. *desert* means "an uncultured region without inhabitants; to abandon"

   dessert means "a sweet course served at the end of a meal"

B. 1. older   6. empathy
   2. adopted   7. farther
   3. healthful   8. birth
   4. number   9. personal
   5. dessert   10. addition

(Sentences are sample responses.)

1. The amount of rainfall last month was one inch.

2. Jim took an upper berth in the train's sleeping car.

3. Todd's elder brother visited this summer.

4. By the fall, we will be much further along in the house renovations.

5. The personnel quota has been increased for the year.

6. Discovering a rare edition of her favorite sonnets excited Dorothy.

7. After many failed attempts to rescue the sunken ship, apathy overcame the crew.

8. Mary Alice found it difficult to adapt to her new school.

9. The doctor told the new parents they had a healthy baby.

10. Hikers discovered a deserted camp and called the authorities.

Vocabulary Practice 27: Commonly Misused Words (p. 27)

A. 1. *ability* means "the power to do something physical or mental"

capacity means "the ability to contain, absorb, or receive and hold"

capacity

2. *advice* means "opinion given as to what to do or how to handle a situation"

advise means "to give advice or an opinion"

advice

3. *affect* means "to influence; to produce a change"

effect means "a result; anything brought about by a cause or agent"

affected

4. *aid* means "to give help or relief"

aide means "an assistant; a helper"

aides

5. *beside* means "at the side of"

besides means "in addition to"

besides

6. *bring* means "to carry or lead to the speaker"

take means "to carry or take away from the speaker"

bring

7. *lose* means "to become unable to find; to bring to ruin or destruction"

loose means "not confined or restrained; free"

loose

8. *site* means "the place where something is, was, or is to be"

sight means "something seen; the act of seeing a view"

cite means "to summon to appear before a court of law; to quote"

sight

9. *strait* means "a narrow waterway connecting two large bodies of water"

straight means "not crooked, bent, or bowed"

strait

10. *among* means "surrounded by; included with"

between means "in or through the space that separates"

between

B. 1. We borrowed large *capacity* pails to wash all the windows.

2. The school counselor gave students *advice* for taking the exam.

3. The *effect* of the factory shutdown was a loss of income for the workers.

4. Earthquake victims needed much *aid* to survive the devastation.

5. *Besides* money, undeveloped countries need education and human services.

6. Each child *took* a homemade treat to the school party.

7. Animals at the local zoo run *loose* within a large protected area.

8. The newspaper article *cited* the mayor's speech on the front page.

9. A *straight* path through the forest led to a beautiful pond.

10. *Among* the four candidates auditioning, Jo, with the most talent, won the part.

Vocabulary Practice 28: Commonly Misused Words (p. 28)

A. 1. r, q
2. o, j
3. s, n
4. e, l
5. t, p
6. h, g
7. a, d
8. c, f
9. m, k
10. i, b

B. 1. allude   6. accepted
2. stationery   7. flounder
3. less than   8. extrinsic
4. imminent   9. abject
5. imply   10. unawares

(Sentences are sample responses.)

1. The candidate tried to *elude* reporters.
2. A *stationary* hot dog cart was set up on the corner.
3. *Fewer than* one hundred people attended the auction.
4. An *eminent* doctor reported his discovery to the association.
5. We *inferred* from the report that the discovery would impact current practices.
6. *Except* for a few details, Sue's term paper was complete.
7. Rock climbers *foundered* temporarily, but were able to continue the climb.
8. Commitment is *intrinsic* to the success of a team's effort in any project.
9. Parents *objected* to the school's early dismissal on a snow day.
10. The small child was *unaware* of the fast-approaching car.

Vocabulary Practice 29: Commonly Misused Words Review (p. 29)

1. amount
2. eminent
3. fewer than
4. advice
5. adapt
6. later
7. lose
8. among
9. stationary
10. formerly
11. desserts
12. affect
13. quite
14. farther
15. beside
16. edition
17. courses
18. minor
19. except
20. infer

B. (Sentences are sample responses.)

1. The doctor *advised* Sue Ellen to stay in bed.
2. Of the two vacation weeks, the *latter* had the better weather.
3. Mike and Jim's parents met *formally* at the game.
4. Dad's bread recipe makes a bread with a *coarse* texture.
5. A coal *miner* was rescued from deep inside the mine.

Vocabulary Practice 30: Specialized Vocabulary (p. 30)

A. 1. plaintiff
   2. appellate court
   3. perjury
   4. defendant
   5. prosecutor
   6. lien
   7. litigation
   8. arraignment
   9. deposition
   10. statute

B. 1. *plagiarism* means "the act of taking ideas, writings, etc. from another and passing them off as one's own"
   2. *larceny* means "the taking of personal property without consent; theft"
   3. *libel* means "any false and malicious written or printed statement to expose a person to ridicule or injure a reputation"
   4. *probate* means "the process of proving before an authorized person that a document is genuine"
   5. *subpoena* means "a written legal order directing a person to appear in court"

C. (Sentences are sample responses.)

1. The plaintiff and her attorney discussed the claim.
2. The claim was appealed in the appellate court.
3. When the witness was cited for perjury, his testimony was dismissed.
4. The bailiff escorted the defendant to the courtroom.
5. An experienced prosecutor presented a strong case for the state.
6. When the homeowners defaulted on their mortgage, the bank put a lien on the property.
7. Litigation costs the state and the defendants great sums of money.

8. The accused appeared in court for their arraignment.
9. Lawyers for the defendant held a deposition.
10. Statutes were cited during the trail to support the defendant's case.

Vocabulary Practice 31: Specialized Vocabulary (p. 31)

A. 1. d 2. g 3. e 4. f 5. i 6. j 7. h 8. c 9. b 10. a

B. 1. hurricane
2. buoy
3. pecan
4. chess
5. bravado
6. shampoo
7. freight
8. gumbo
9. mattress
10. jungle

C. 1. *al fresco*: Italian, *al fresco*; means "outdoors"
2. *saute*: French, *salter*; from Latin, *saltare*; means "to cook quickly in a small amount of butter and oil over a high flame"
3. *impeach*: Latin, *in pedica* (foot); means "to challenge or discredit; to bring before a tribunal"

4. *coach*: Hungarian, *kocsi*; means "a large, covered, four-wheel carriage; the low-priced class of accommodations in transportation; an instructor or trainer"
5. *umbrella*: Latin, *umbra*; means "a screen or shade, usually made of material stretched over a folding frame for protection against rain or sun"
6. *treat*: Latin, *tractare*; means "to discuss terms; to negotiate; to deal with a subject in writing or speech; to act or behave toward in a specific manner"
7. *talisman*: Greek, *telos*; means "something such as a ring thought to bring good luck"
8. *knapsack*: Dutch, *knapzak*; means "a bag or case worn on the back for carrying equipment or supplies"
9. *Chicago*: Algonquian, *Chicago* ("place of the onion"); means a city and port in Illinois on Lake Michigan"
10. *vanilla*: Spanish, *vainilla*; means "any of a genus of climbing tropical American orchids with fragrant greenish-yellow flowers; an extract of the vanilla capsule"

Spelling Practice 1: Words With *ei* and *ie* (p. 32)

A. 1. Sample answer
2. conceit — except after c
3. reimburse — two syllables
4. efficient — exception
5. caffeine — exception
6. piety — two syllables
7. deceit — except after c
8. conceive — except after c
9. species — exception
10. impropriety — two syllables
11. receipt — except after c
12. inveigh — when sounded like a

13. yield — i before e
14. brief — i before e
15. perceive — except after c
16. friend — i before e
17. gaiety — i before e
18. surveillance — when sounded like a
19. belief — i before e
20. variety — i before e
21. sheik — when sounded like a
22. retrieve — i before e
23. sufficient — exception
24. ancient — exception
25. fiefdom — i before e

B. 1. weird

2. neither

3. proficient

4. conscience

5. leisure

Spelling Practice 2: Final *e* With Suffixes
(p. 33)

A. 1. arranged   1

2. upgrading   1

3. encouragement   3

4. hopeful   3

5. ninety   3

6. serviceable   2

7. erased   1

8. tasteful   3

9. advantageous   2

10. writing   1

B. 1. achieved

2. comparing

3. rehearsal

4. removable

5. remorseful

6. argument

7. safety

8. outrageous

9. thriving

10. approval

Spelling Practice 3: Final *y* With Suffixes
(p. 34)

A. 1. legacies

2. beautifying

3. daily

4. magnified

5. employable

6. tardiness

7. haughtily

8. testifying

9. mystifies

10. cheerily

11. simplified

12. charitable

13. heaviness

14. fortifying

15. societies

16. spryly

17. scurried

18. spunkiness

19. liquefied

20. verifiable

21. justifying

22. heartily

23. qualifies

24. occupying

25. dizziness

26. memorable

27. uncannily

28. apologies

29. relaying

30. allied

B.

Change *y* to *i*	Retain *y*	Exceptions
legacies	beautifying	daily
magnified	employable	charitable
tardiness	testifying	memorable
haughtily	fortifying	
mystifies	spryly	
cheerily	justifying	
simplified	occupying	
heaviness	relaying	
societies		
scurried		
spunkiness		
liquefied		
verifiable		
heartily		
qualifies		
dizziness		
uncannily		
apologies		
allied		

Spelling Practice 4: Words Ending in *l* and *ll*
(p. 35)

A. 1. frill

2. conceal

3. vertical

4. appeal

5. theatrical

6. real

7. whirl

8. chlorophyll

9. sprawl

10. dismal

11. thrill

12. repeal

13. shawl

14. Brazil

15. quill

16. kneel

17. snarl

18. goodwill

19. whippoorwill

20. daffodil

B.	Rule 1/*call*	Rule 2/*seal*	Rule 3/*crawl*	Rule 4/*special*/*treadmill*
	frill	real	whirl	conceal
	thrill	kneel	sprawl	vertical
	quill		shawl	appeal
			snarl	theatrical
				chlorophyll
				dismal
				repeal
				Brazil
				goodwill
				whippoorwill
				daffodil

Adding five more words:

B.	Rule 1/*call*	Rule 2/*seal*	Rule 3/*crawl*	Rule 4/*special*/*treadmill*
	1. shrill	1. reel	1. pearl	1. extoll
	2. scroll	2. deal	2. twirl	2. appall
	3. stall	3. haul	3. trawl	3. instill
	4. drill	4. drool	4. gnarl	4. carpal
	5. knoll	5. mail	5. curl	5. entail

Spelling Practice 5: Double the Final Consonant (pp. 36–37)

A.

1. relaxed	4	11. morally	2
2. grinning	1	12. appointment	3
3. accidentally	2	13. shyness	4
4. commitment	2	14. paralleling	2
5. retractable	3	15. permitted	2
6. candidness	2	16. patroller	2
7. expounded	3	17. propelling	2
8. planned	1	18. literally	2
9. importer	3	19. thickly	3
10. submitted	2	20. entrapment	2

B.

1. disjointed
2. √
3. discovering
4. √
5. benefiting
6. overcommitted

7. √
8. stacking
9. contentment
10. √
11. loyally
12. flowing
13. wrapped
14. extractable
15. soundness
16. rationally
17. canceled (cancelled, alternate spelling)
18. traveler (traveller, alternate spelling)
19. commendable
20. forgetful
21. objected
22. repellent
23. √
24. correctness
25. √
26. transferring
27. amendment
28. renewed
29. squawking
30. √

C. Spelling Rule 1	Spelling Rule 2	Spelling Rule 3	Spelling Rule 4
clotted	beginner	disjointed	flowing
wrapped	discovering	enrichment	taxing
	benefiting	stacking	renewed
	overcommitted	contentment	squawking
	loyally	confidently	stacking
	rationally	extractable	
	canceled	soundness	
	traveler	commendable	
	forgetful	objected	
	repellent	remarkable	
	transferring	correctness	
	regrettable	amendment	

D. Adding five more words:

Spelling Rule 1	Spelling Rule 2	Spelling Rule 3	Spelling Rule 4
1. swapped	1. rebelled	1. responded	1. taxable
2. scrubbed	2. combatting	2. rewarding	2. lawful
3. plotted	3. occurring	3. surrounded	3. payment
4. flagged	4. remitted	4. assignment	4. annoying
5. chipped	5. employment	5. resulting	5. wallowed

Spelling Practice 6: Words Ending in -cede, -ceed, -sede (p. 38)

A.
1. precede
2. recede
3. intercede
4. secede
5. accede
6. concede
7. proceed
8. succeed
9. exceed
10. supersede

1. *precede* means "to be, come, or go before in time, place, rank or importance"
2. *recede* means "to go or move back; to withdraw"
3. *intercede* means "to plead or make a request in behalf of another or others"
4. *secede* means "to withdraw formally from membership in, or association with, a group or organization"
5. *accede* means "to give in; to agree with"

6. *concede* means "to admit as true or valid; to acknowledge"
7. *proceed* means 'to advance or go on after stopping or an interruption"
8. *succeed* means "to come next after another; to follow"
9. *exceed* means "to be beyond or go beyond; to be more than or greater than"
10. *supersede* means "to cause to be set aside or dropped from use as inferior or obsolete and replaced by something else"

B.
1. intercede
2. acceded
3. exceeded
4. proceeded
5. recede
6. supersedes
7. conceded
8. secede
9. succeed
10. precedes

Spelling Practice 7: Words Ending in -el and -le (p. 39)

A.
1. pinnacle
2. humble
3. monocle
4. fizzle
5. parcel
6. squirrel
7. ripple
8. principle
9. hobble
10. √
11. icicle
12. √
13. frazzle
14. √
15. marvel
16. sorrel
17. cripple
18. vehicle
19. whistle
20. barrel
21. subtle
22. hazel
23. √
24. trickle
15. √
26. hostel
27. √
28. spectacle
29. tremble
30. triangle

B.

Rule 1	Rule 2	Rule 3	Rule 4
squirrel	parcel	humble	pinnacle
barrel		ripple	monocle
libel		principle	fizzle
chapel		hobble	icicle
hostel		trouble	frazzle
duffel		noble	vehicle
minstrel		cripple	hazel
marvel		whistle	trickle
sorrel		subtle	spectacle
		tremble	
		triangle	

C.
1. 3 — fiddle, tangle
2. 2 — parcel, cancel
3. 3 — nibble, brittle
4. 3 — grapple, trample
5. 3 — cradle, propel (exception)
6. 3 — simple, maple
7. 3 — ripple, throttle
8. 1 — marvel, novel
9. 1 — panel, hostel
10. 3 — tangle, shingle
11. 1 — sorrel, tinsel
12. 1 — pummel, trowel
13. 4 — trickle, snorkel (exception)
14. 4 — tackle, fizzle
15. 3 — assemble, waffle

D. (Sentences are sample responses.)

Rule 1 Our book club will discuss a new novel next week.

Rule 2 The overnight mail service delivered a parcel next door.

Rule 3 Students with reports will assemble in the auditorium.

Rule 3 Exception We watched the clown propel himself through the air and land on his feet.

Rule 4 On a rainy day, Sandy likes to tackle her closets.

Rule 3 Exception Don put on snorkel gear and jumped into the water.

Spelling Practice 8: Words Ending in -er and -re (p. 41)

A.
1. confer
2. farther
3. theater
4. character
5. sequester
6. linger
7. meager
8. cloister
9. acre
10. engender
11. zither
12. shoulder
13. leather
14. trailer
15. macabre
16. decipher
17. toddler
18. refer
19. mediocre
20. philosopher
21. meander
22. ogre
23. massacre
24. mariner
25. genre
26. feather
27. timber
28. center
29. answer
30. photographer

B. *theater* and *theatre*
meager and *meagre*
center and *centre*

C. (Sample responses)
1. leather
2. character
3. photographer
4. toddler
5. mariner
6. decipher
7. mediocre
8. genre
9. acre
10. theater

Spelling Practice 9: Commonly Misspelled Words (p. 42)

A.

1. abbreviate	16. occasion
2. accidentally	17. parallel
3. accumulate	18. possess
4. bulletin	19. succeed
5. committee	20. √
6. planning	21. syllable
7. scissors	22. tomorrow
8. embarrass	23. villain
9. √	24. √
10. exaggerate	25. √
11. grammar	26. √
12. immigrant	27. regrettable
13. misspell	28. correspondence
14. √	29. √
15. disappoint	30. flannel

B. Sample responses.

1. *planing* means "making smooth"
   planning means "devising a scheme for doing, making, or arranging"
2. *taped* means "bound by tape; recorded sound, video, computer material"
   tapped means "struck lightly"
3. *riper* means "more fully grown or advanced"
   ripper means "a person or thing that rips"
4. *hoping* means "wanting or expecting"
   hopping means "moving by leaping or springing on one or all feet at once"
5. *griper* means "something that holds;" also "a complainer"
   gripper means "something that holds firmly"
6. *mating* means "forming as a pair"
   matting means "covering with a mat" also "tangling into a thick mass"
7. *striped* means "marked with a stripe"
   stripped means "pulled or torn off" also "broken or damaged"

Spelling Practice 10: Commonly Misspelled Words (p. 43)

A.

1. achieve	7. height
2. aerial	8. despair
3. √	9. eighth
4. anxiety	10. foreign
5. √	11. appease
6. turmoil	12. bemoan

13. √	22. receiving
14. √	23. ingenious
15. beleaguer	24. cloister
16. assuage	25. copious
17. boisterous	26. dissuade
18. √	27. naïve
19. variety	28. √
20. cheaper	29. persuade
21. glamorous	30. √

B.
1. height, eighth, foreign, receiving
2. achieve, anxiety, variety
3. aisle, despair. prosaic, naïve
4. aerial, aviary, pliable
5. assuage, dissuade, persuade
6. appease, beleaguer, cheaper
7. bemoan, approach
8. turmoil, cloister, boisterous
9. boisterous, glamorous, infamous
10. amphibious, ingenious, copious

Spelling Practice Review (p. 44)

A.

1. abbreviate	26. √
2. embarrass	27. occasion
3. enamel	28. reference
4. exaggerate	29. syllable
5. conifer	30. √
6. parallel	31. achieve
7. beautifying	32. liquefy
8. possesses	33. immigrant
9. disappoint	34. allowance
10. √	35. anxiety
11. √	36. √
12. misspell	37. judgmental
13. ambivalence	38. resonance
14. benevolence	39. variety
15. tardiness	40. character
16. √	41. hindrance
17. nuisance	42. delineate
18. resistance	43. impervious
19. admittance	44. compel
20. acquaintance	45. succeed
21. attendance	46. divergence
22. spectacle	47. √
23. aerial	48. accidentally
24. conscience	49. argumentative
25. simplified	50. circuitous

51. scalpel	56. √
52. sagacious	57. genteel
53. naïve	58. discreet
54. acknowledgement	59. prophecy
55. unwieldy	60. fallible

B. (Some words are listed in two categories.)

Double Medial Consonants
abbreviate
embarrass
exaggerate
parallel
possesses
disappoint
grammar
committee
misspell
admittance
attendance
occasion
syllable
immigrant
allowance
succeed
accidentally
fallible

-el or -le
enamel
parallel
spectacle
compel
scalpel
fallible

-er or -re
conifer
linger

y to i/retain y
beautifying
tardiness
annoyed
simplified

-ance or -ence
ambivalence
benevolence
independence
resistance
acquaintance
resonance
hindrance
divergence
reference

-cy or -sy
prophecy

silent consonant
character
foreign

-cede
precede

i before e rule
achieve
anxiety
variety
grief

two medial vowels
succeed
nuisance
aerial
liquefy
delineate
impervious
foreign
circuitous
sagacious
naïve
unwieldy
genteel
discreet

drop e/retain e
judgmental
argumentative
acknowledgment